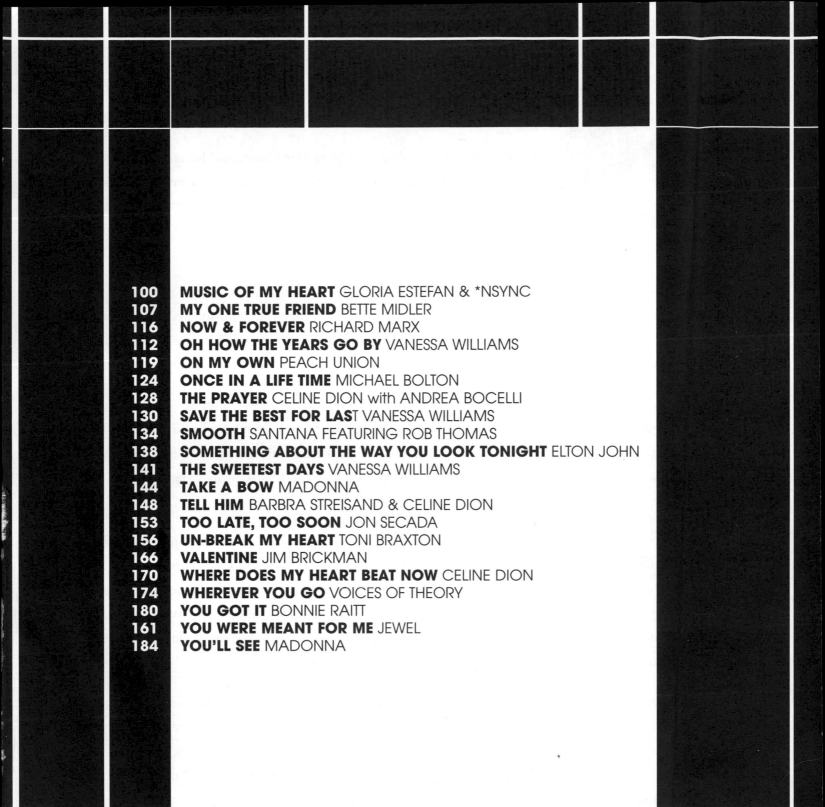

Dan Coates ❑❑❑❑❑❑❑❑❑❑❑❑❑❑❑❑❑❑

As a student at the University of Miami, Dan Coates paid his tuition by playing the piano at south Florida nightclubs and restaurants. One evening in 1975, after Dan had worked his unique brand of magic on the ivories, a stranger from the music field walked up and told him that he should put his inspired piano arrangements down on paper so they could be published.

Dan took the stranger's advice—and the world of music has become much richer as a result. Since that chance encounter long ago, Dan has gone on to achieve international acclaim for his brilliant piano arrangements. His *Big Note, Easy Piano* and *Professional Touch* arrangements have inspired countless piano students and established themselves as classics against which all other works must be measured.

Enjoying an exclusive association with Warner Bros. Publications since 1982, Dan has demonstrated a unique gift for writing arrangements intended for students of every level, from beginner to advanced. Dan never fails to bring a fresh and original approach to his work. Pushing his own creative boundaries with each new manuscript, he writes material that is musically exciting and educationally sound.

From the very beginning of his musical life, Dan has always been eager to seek new challenges. As a five-year-old in Syracuse, New York, he used to sneak into the home of his neighbors to play their piano. Blessed with an amazing ear for music, Dan was able to imitate the melodies of songs he had heard on the radio. Finally, his neighbors convinced his parents to buy Dan his own piano. At that point, there was no stopping his musical development. Dan won a prestigious New York State competition for music composers at the age of 15. Then, after graduating from high school, he toured the world as an arranger and pianist with the group Up With People.

Later, Dan studied piano at the University of Miami with the legendary Ivan Davis, developing his natural abilities to stylize music on the keyboard. Continuing to perform professionally during and after his college years, Dan has played the piano on national television and at the 1984 Summer Olympics in Los Angeles. He has also accompanied recording artists as diverse as Dusty Springfield and Charlotte Rae.

During his long and prolific association with Warner Bros. Publications, Dan has written many award-winning books. He conducts piano workshops worldwide, demonstrating his famous arrangements with a special spark that never fails to inspire students and teachers alike.

Contents

A Decade of Lite Hits
Contemporary Pop Ballads

Arranged by
DAN COATES

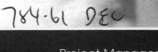

Project Manager: Carol Cuellar
Editorial Assistant: Donna Salzburg
Book Art Layout: Design O'Rama

DAN COATES® is a registered trademark of Warner Bros. Publications

'cause we've got a life of love
a sec - ond to give to me

that won't ev - er change.
that mag - ic you make. } And

ev - 'ry day ———— love me your own spe - cial way. Melt all my

heart ———— a - way ——— with a smile.

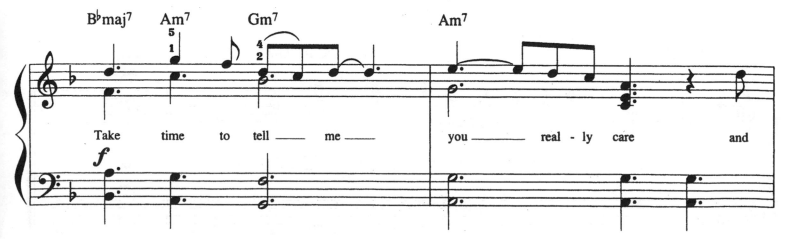

Take time to tell —— me ———— you ———— real - ly care and

AMAZED

Words and Music by
MARV GREEN, AIMEE MAYO
and CHRIS LINDSEY
Arranged by DAN COATES

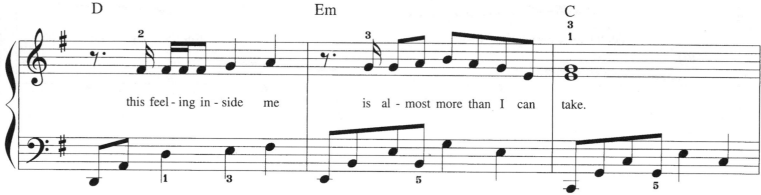

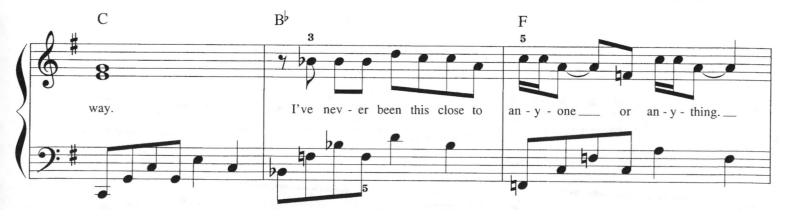

14

I can hear your thoughts,   I can see your ___ dreams.

Chorus:

I don't know how you do what you do. ___   I'm so in love with

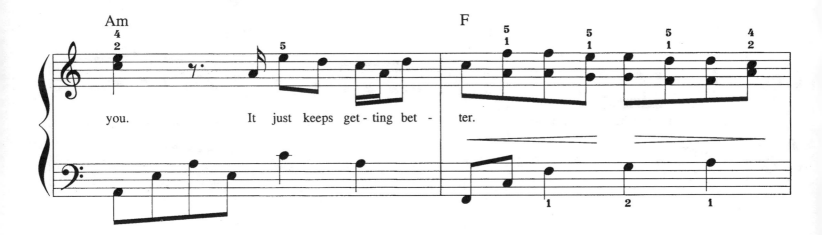

you.   It just keeps get - ting bet - ter.

I wan - na spend the rest of my life ___   with you by my side ___

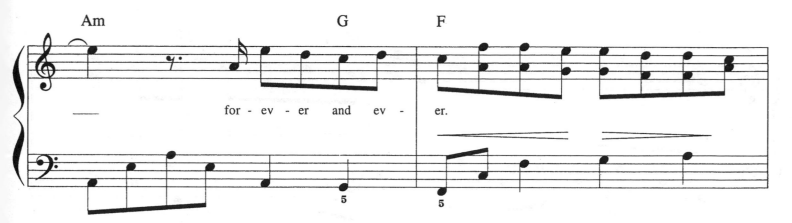

for - ev - er and ev - er.

Ev -'ry lit - tle thing that you do, ba - by, I'm a - mazed by

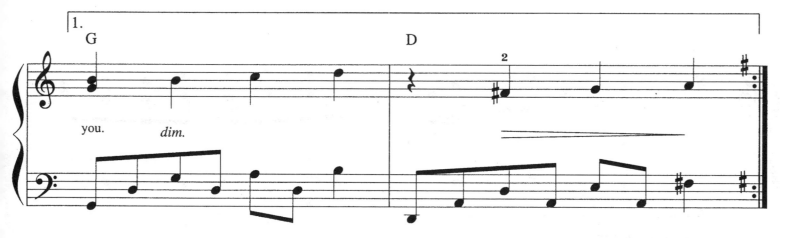

1.

you. *dim.*

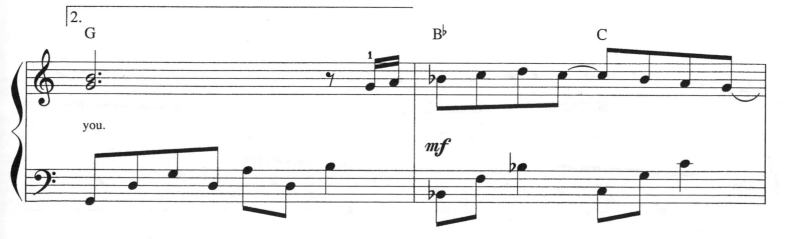

2.

you.

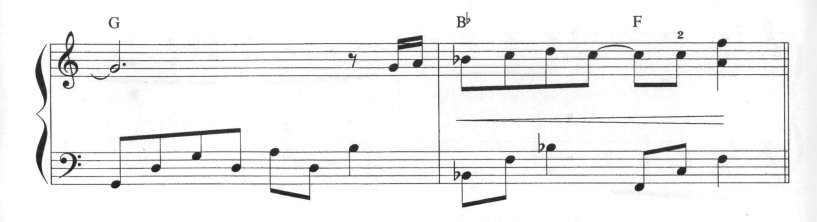

Ev -'ry lit - tle thing that you do,____ I'm so in love with

you. It just keeps get - ting bet - ter.

I wan - na spend the rest of my life____ with you by my side____

Verse 2:
The smell of your skin,
The taste of your kiss,
The way you whisper in the dark.
Your hair all around me,
Baby, you surround me.
You touch every place in my heart.
Oh, it feels like the first time every time.
I wanna spend the whole night in your eyes.
(To Chorus:)

ANGEL OF MINE

Words and Music by
RHETT LAWRENCE and TRAVON POTTS
Arranged by DAN COATES

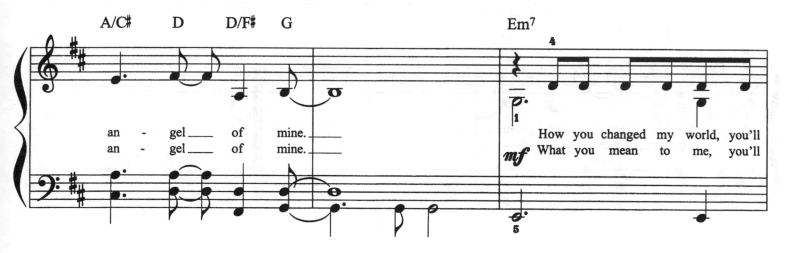

20

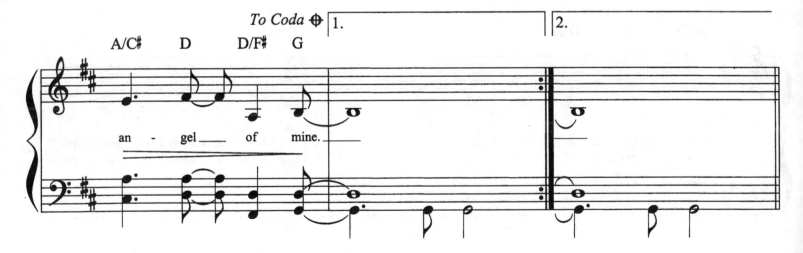

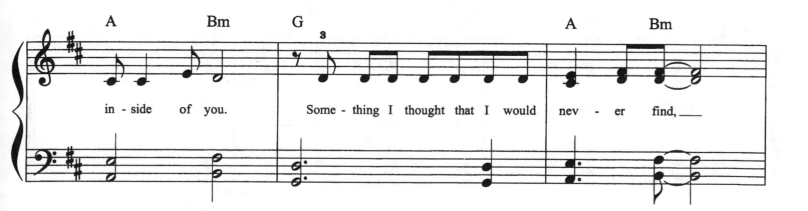

D.S. 𝄋 *al Coda*

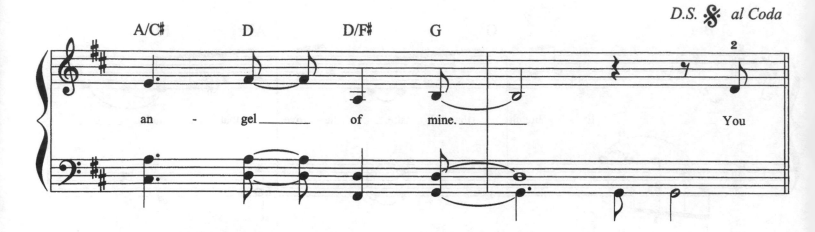

an - gel _____ of mine. _____ You

Coda

_____ I look at you look - ing at me. _____

mf

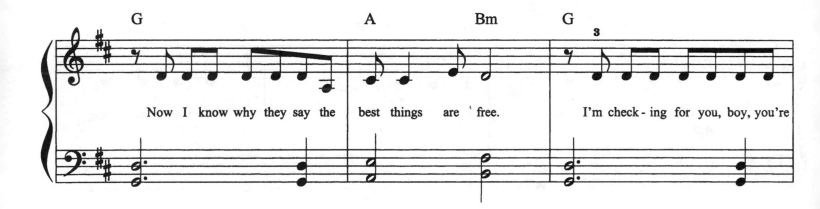

Now I know why they say the best things are 'free. I'm check - ing for you, boy, you're

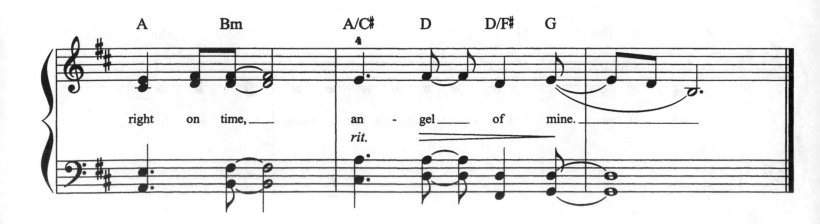

right on time, _____ an - gel _____ of mine. _____

rit.

Theme from "UP CLOSE & PERSONAL"

BECAUSE YOU LOVED ME

Words and Music by
DIANE WARREN
Arranged by DAN COATES

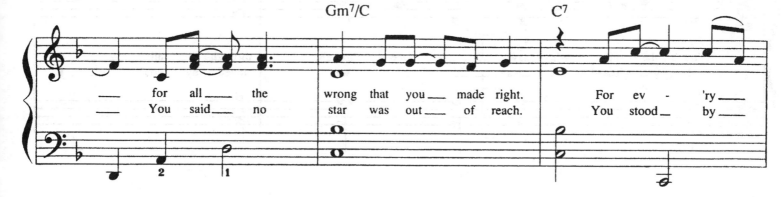

be for - ev - er thank - ful, ba - by. You're the one ___ who held ___
grate - ful for ___ each day ___ you gave me. May - be I ___ don't know ___

___ me up, ___ nev - er let ___ me fall.
___ that much, ___ but I know this much ___ is true:

You're the one ___ who saw ___ me through, through it all. ___
I was blessed ___ be - cause ___ I was loved by you. ___

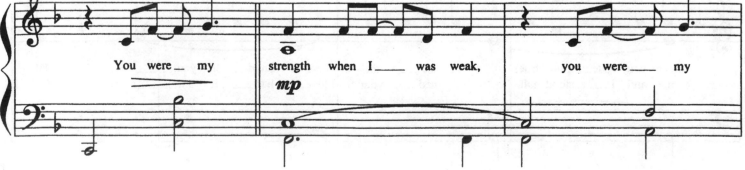

You were ___ my strength when I ___ was weak, you were ___ my

voice when I could-n't speak. You were___ my eyes when I could-n't see,___

___ you saw___ the best there was___ in me. Lift-ed___ me___

up when I could-n't reach, you gave___ me faith 'cause you___ be-lieved.___

To Coda ⊕

I'm ev-'ry-thing___ I am___ be-cause___ you

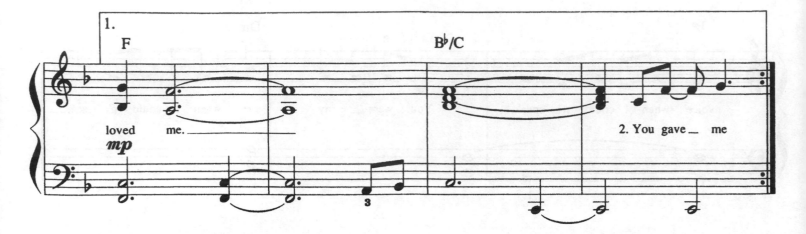

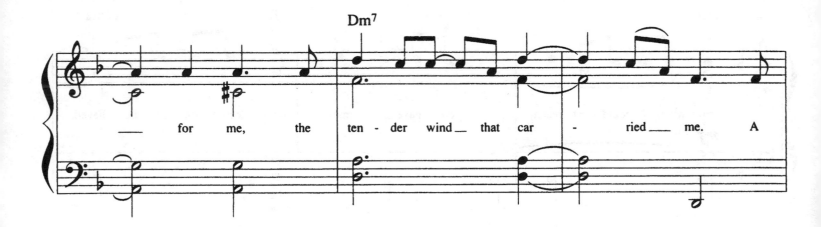

BY HEART

Composed by
JIM BRICKMAN and
HOLLYE LEVEN
Arranged by DAN COATES

Hold me close, ___ ba - by, ___ please. ___
When you go, ___ I'll stop ___ the clock. ___

Tell me an - y - thing but that you're gon - na leave.
I won't ev - er let this mo - ment stop.

As I kiss ___ this fall - en tear, ___ I pro - mise you I will be ___
Time is steal - in' you from me, ___ but it can nev - er take this mem - o -

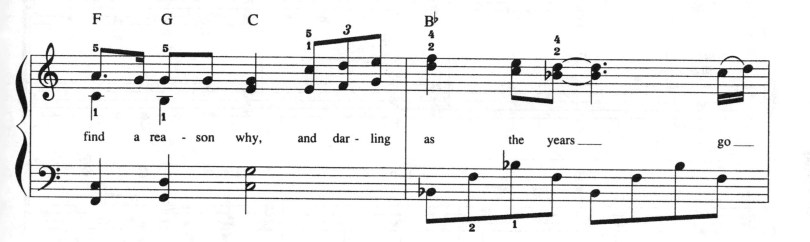

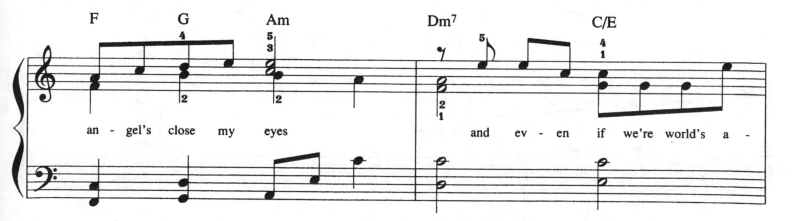

Em/A   A⁷   Dm⁷   G⁷sus⁴   G   *To Coda* ⊕

part,   I'll find my way   back to you   by

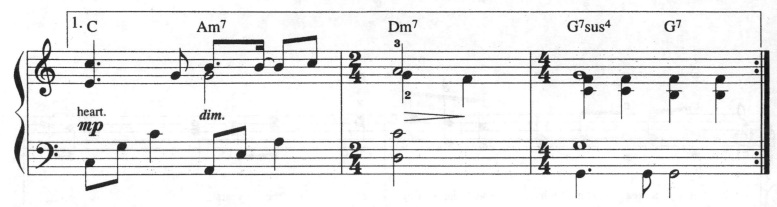

1. C   Am⁷   Dm⁷   G⁷sus⁴   G⁷

heart.   *mp*   *dim.*

2. C   Am⁷   Dm⁷   G⁷sus⁴   G⁷   *D.S.* 𝄋 *al Coda*

heart.   *mp*   Un - til the

Coda ⊕   C   Am⁷   Dm⁷   G

heart.   *mp*

C   Am   Dm⁷   G⁷   C

rit. e dim.   *p*

COUNT ON ME

Words and Music by
BABYFACE, WHITNEY HOUSTON
and **MICHAEL HOUSTON**
Arranged by DAN COATES

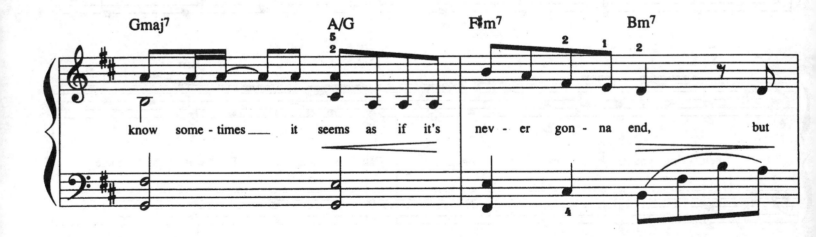

D   Em⁷   D/F♯   G

count on me ___ through thick and thin, a friend - ship that ___ will nev - er end. When

D/A   A/G   D/F♯   G

you are weak, ___ I will be strong, help - ing you ___ to car - ry on. ___

D/A   Bm   Em   F♯   Bm

Call on me, ___ I will be there. Don't be a - fraid.

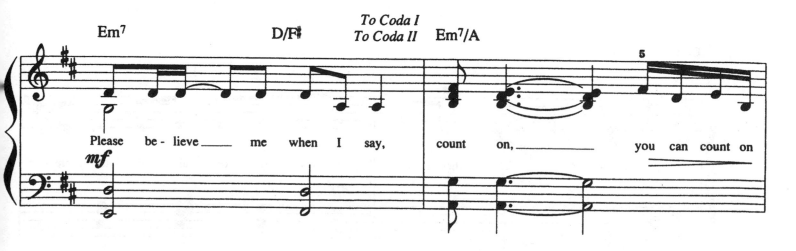

Em⁷   D/F♯   *To Coda I*   Em⁷/A

To Coda II

Please be - lieve ___ me when I say, count on, ___ you can count on

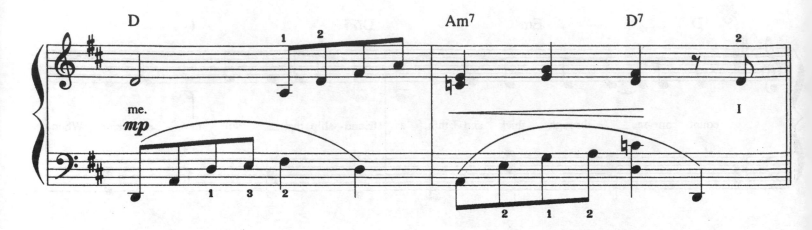

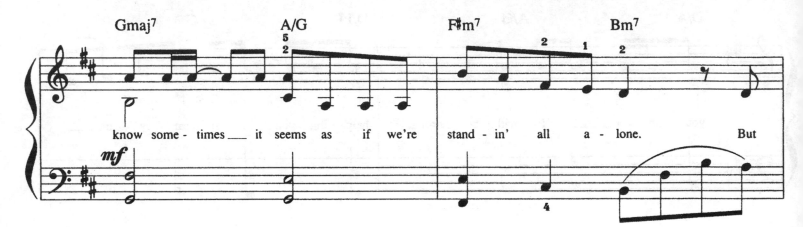

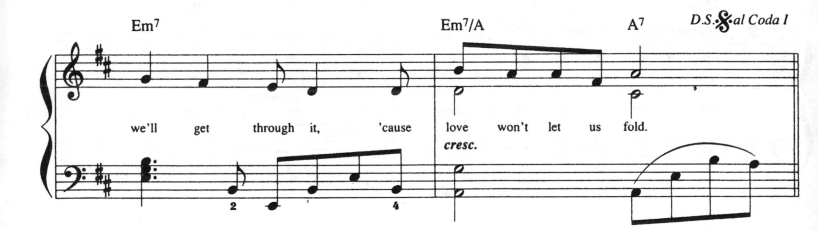

DREAMING OF YOU

Words and Music by
TOM SNOW and
FRAN GOLDE
Arranged by DAN COATES

Moderately slow

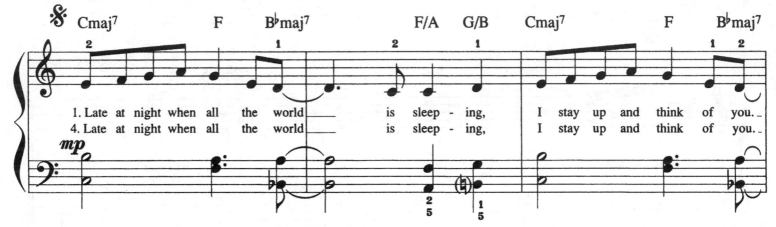

1. Late at night when all the world____ is sleep-ing, I stay up and think of you.____
4. Late at night when all the world____ is sleep-ing, I stay up and think of you.____

And I wish on a star____ that some-where you are____ think-ing
And I still can't be-lieve____ that you came up to me____ and said,

of me, too.____ 'Cause I'm dream - ing____ of
"I love you."____ I love you, too.____ Now, I'm dream - ing____ with

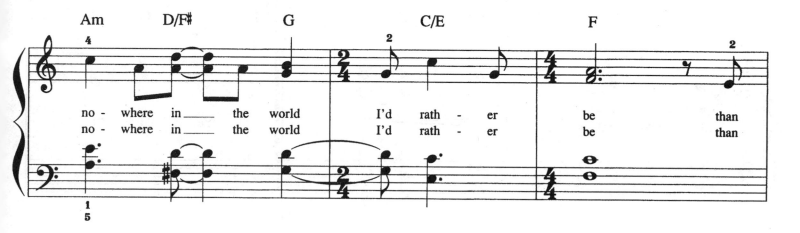

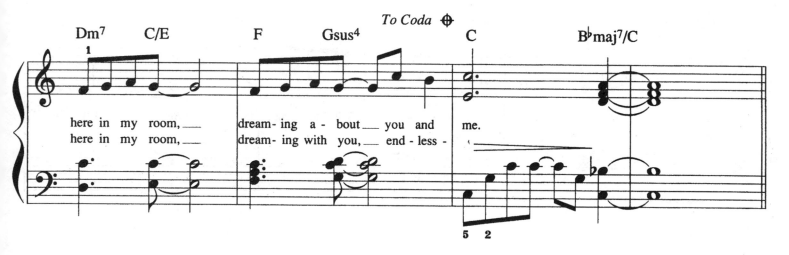

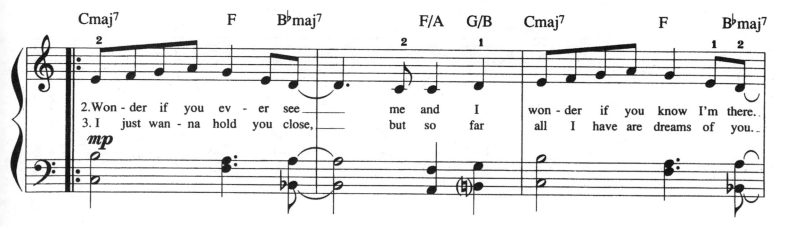

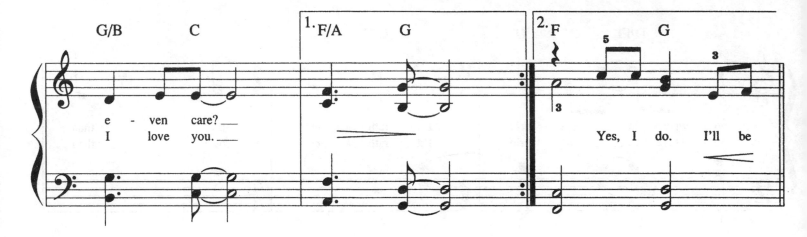

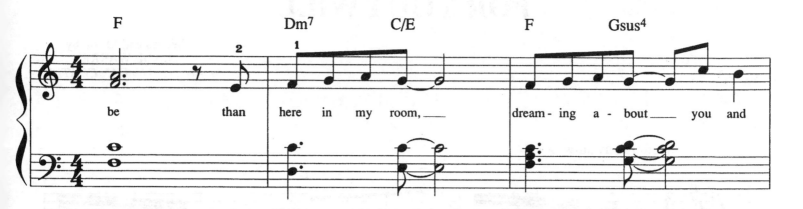

D.S. 𝄋 al Coda ⊕

FOR YOU I WILL

Words and Music by
DIANE WARREN
Arranged by DAN COATES

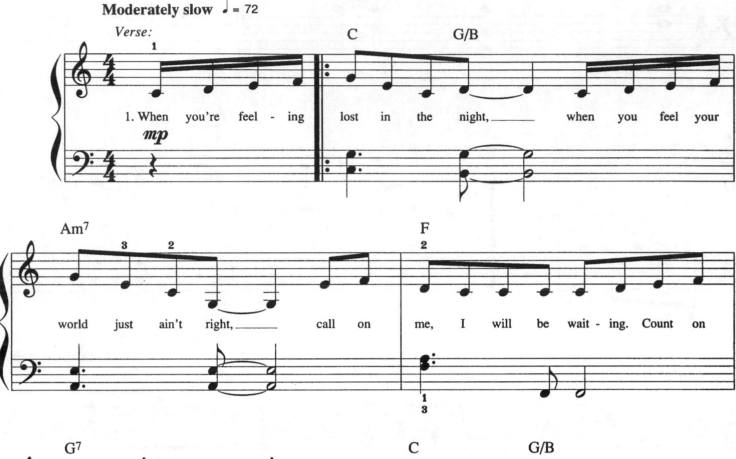

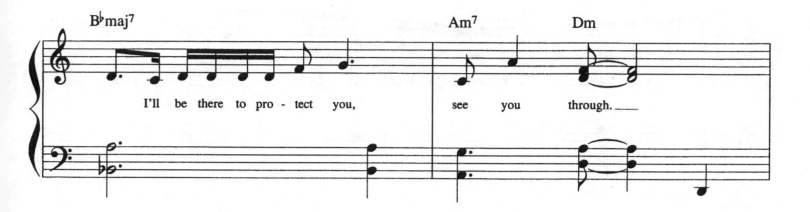

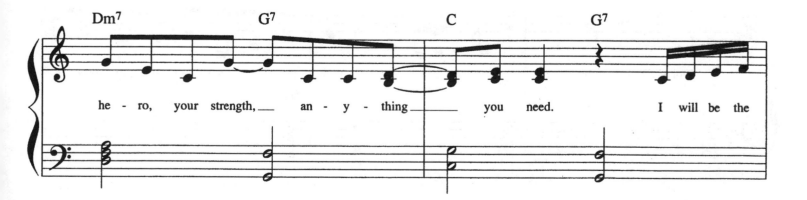

42

sun in your sky,_____ I will light your way for all time,_____ prom - ise

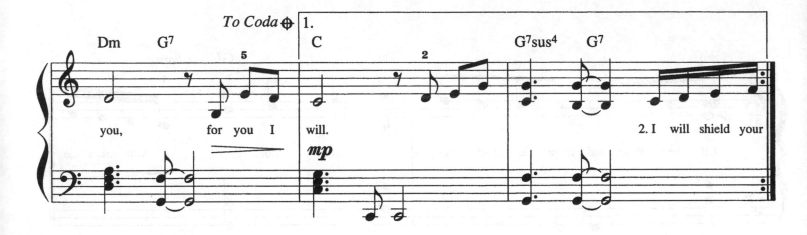

you, for you I will. 2. I will shield your

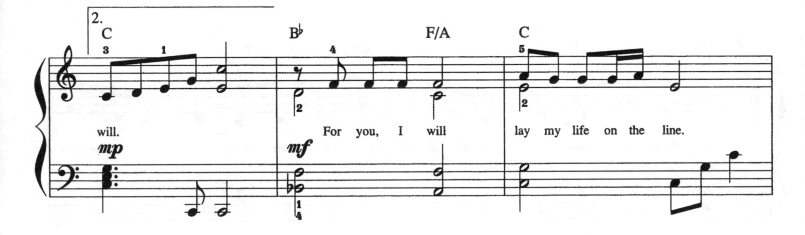

will. For you, I will lay my life on the line.

For you, I'll fight, for you, I will die. With ev - 'ry breath, with all my soul, I

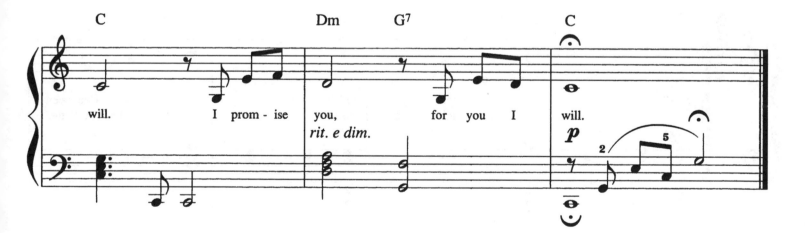

Verse 2:
I will shield your heart from the rain,
I won't let no harm come your way.
Oh, these arms will be your shelter,
No, these arms won't let you down.
If there is a mountain to move,
I will move that mountain for you.
I'm here for you, I'm here forever.
I will be a fortress, tall and strong.
I'll keep you safe, I'll stand beside you,
Right or wrong.   *(To Chorus:)*

From the Twentieth Century-Fox Motion Picture "ONE FINE DAY"

FOR THE FIRST TIME

Words and Music by
JAMES NEWTON HOWARD,
ALLAN RICH and JUD FRIEDMAN
Arranged by DAN COATES

Slowly ♩ = 62

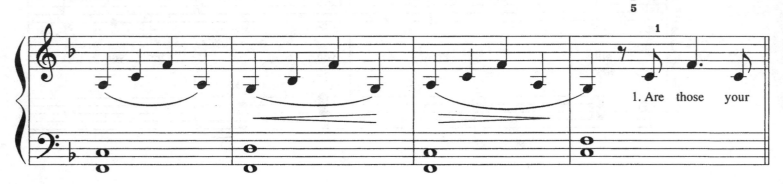

1. Are those your

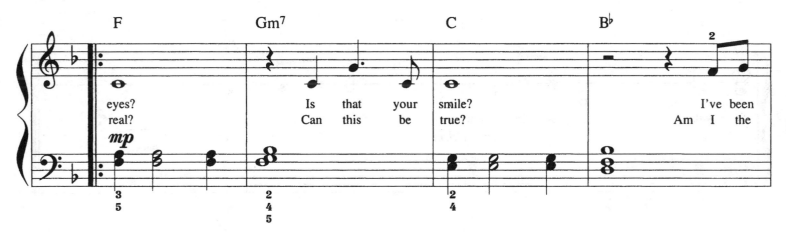

eyes? / real?   Is that your / Can this be   smile? / true?   I've been / Am I the

look-ing at you for-ev-er, yet I / per-son I was this morn-ing, and are   nev-er saw you be-fore. / you the same ___ you?   Are these your / It's all so

HANDS

Words and Music by
JEWEL KILCHER and
PATRICK LEONARD
Arranged by DAN COATES

1. If I could tell the world just one thing, it would be that we're all o-kay.

And not to wor-ry 'cause wor-ry is waste-ful and use-

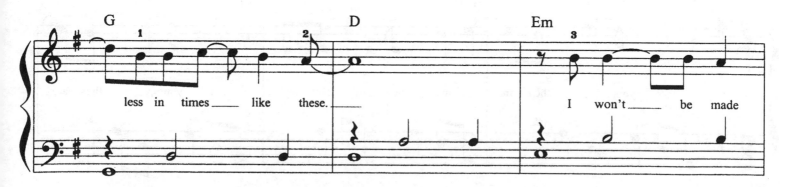

less in times like these. I won't be made

C   **G**   **D**

use - less. ___   I won't be i - dle with des - pair.

Em   **C**   **G**

I'll gather my - self a - round ___ my faith, ___ for light does the dark - ness most

Chorus:

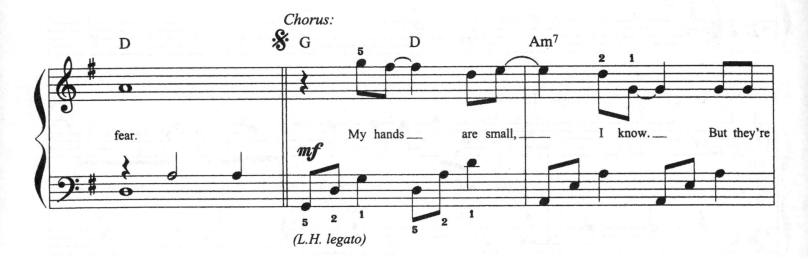

D   **G**   **D**   **Am⁷**

fear.   My hands ___ are small, ___ I know. ___ But they're

mf

(L.H. legato)

G   **D**   **Am⁷**   **G**   **D**

not yours, ___ they are ___ my own. ___ But they're not yours, ___ they are ___

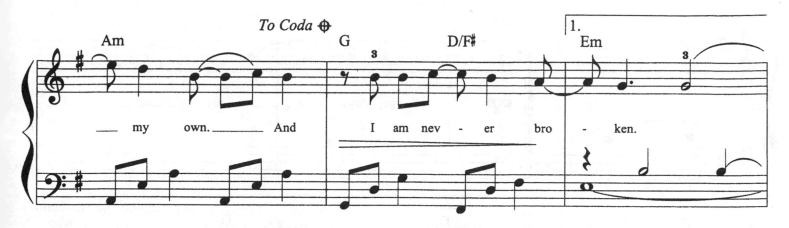

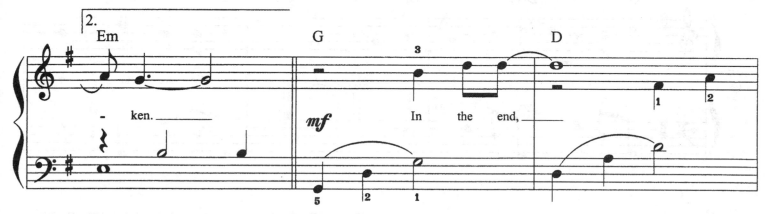

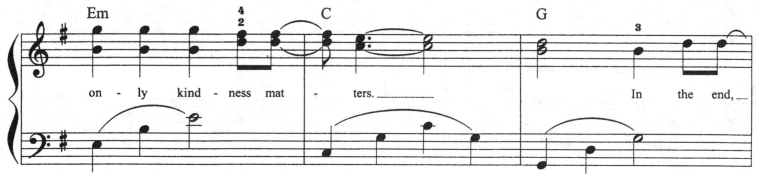

52

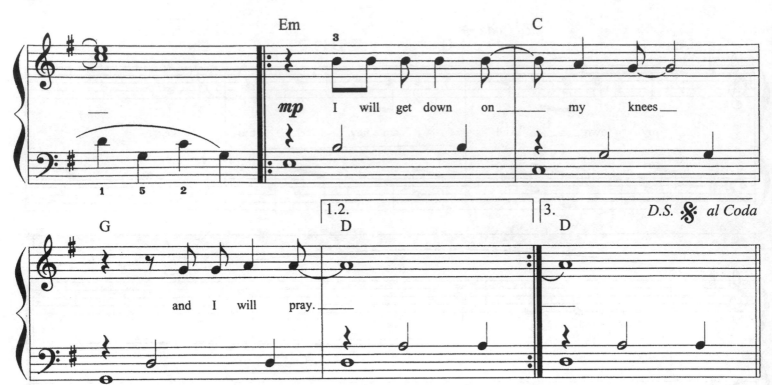

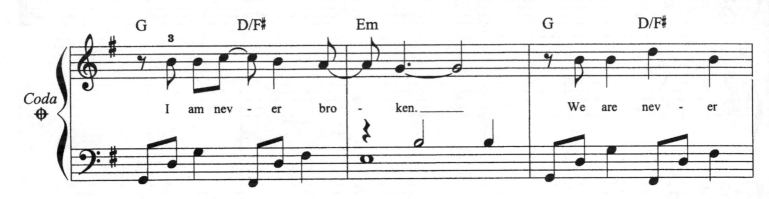

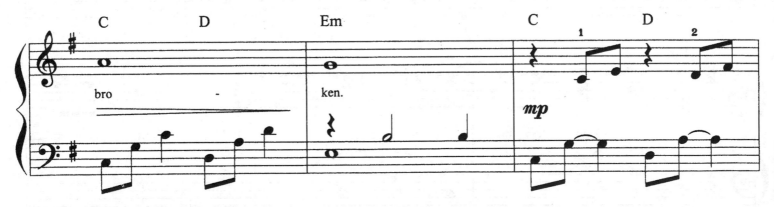

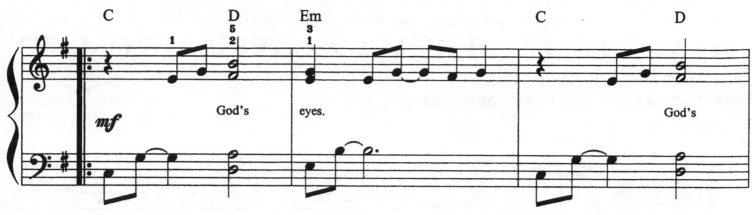

Verse 2:
Poverty stole your golden shoes,
It didn't steal your laughter.
And heartache came to visit me,
But I knew it wasn't ever after.
We'll fight not out of spite,
For someone must stand up for what's right.
'Cause where there's a man who has no voice,
There ours shall go on singing.
(To Chorus:)

From the Original Motion Picture Soundtrack "DON JUAN DeMARCO"

HAVE YOU EVER REALLY LOVED A WOMAN?

Lyrics by
BRYAN ADAMS and ROBERT JOHN "MUTT" LANGE

Music by
MICHAEL KAMEN
Arranged by DAN COATES

55

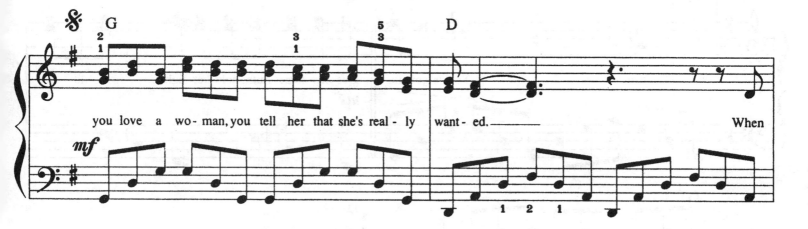

tell me have you ev-er real-ly, real-ly, real-ly ev-er loved a wo - man?— 2. To real-ly— love a

wo - man?— You've got to give her some faith, hold her tight, a lit - tle

ten - der- ness, you've got to treat her — right. She will be there for you, tak-ing good care of

you. And when you

From the Motion Picture "THE PREACHER'S WIFE"

I BELIEVE IN YOU AND ME

Words and Music by
SANDY LINZER and DAVID WOLFERT
Arranged by DAN COATES

59

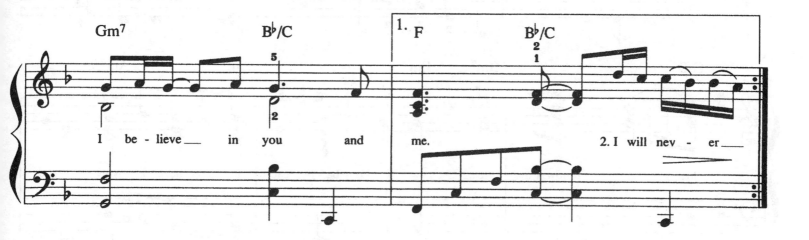

Freely

me.
See, I'm lost, _____ now I'm free, _____ 'cause

I be-lieve in you and ___ me.

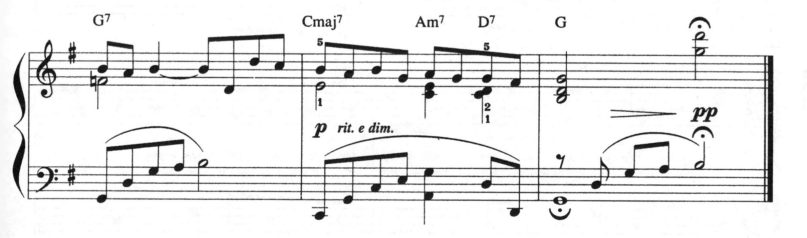

Verse 2:
I will never leave your side,
I will never hurt your pride.
When all the chips are down,
I will always be around
Just to be right where you are, my love.
Oh, I love you, boy.
I will never leave you out,
I will always let you in
To places no one has ever been.
Deep inside, can't you see?
I believe in you and me.

From Touchstone Pictures' "ARMAGEDDON"

I DON'T WANT TO MISS A THING

Words and Music by
DIANE WARREN
Arranged by DAN COATES

1st time only

G   D/F#   Em

stay lost in this mo - ment for - ev - er.   Ev - 'ry mo - ment

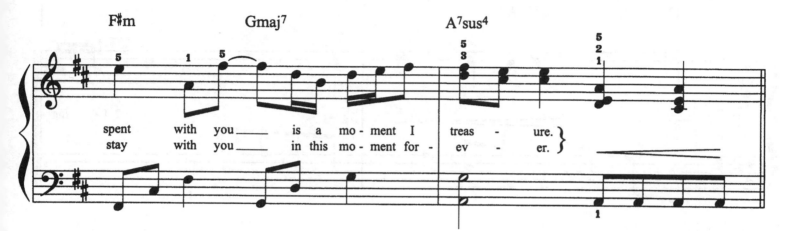

F#m   Gmaj7   A7sus4

spent with you____ is a mo - ment I treas - ure. }
stay with you____ in this mo - ment for - ev - er. }

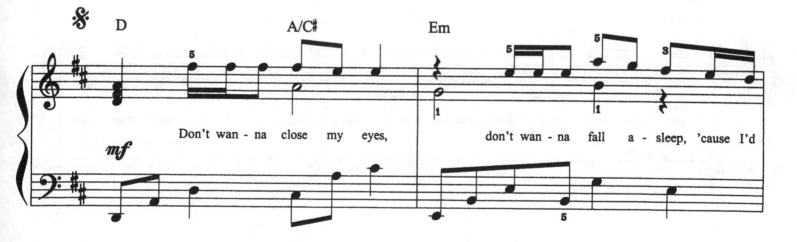

D   A/C#   Em

mf

Don't wan - na close my eyes,   don't wan - na fall a - sleep, 'cause I'd

G   A7   D   A/C#

miss you, babe, and I don't wan - na miss a thing.____ 'Cause e - ven when I dream of you,

64

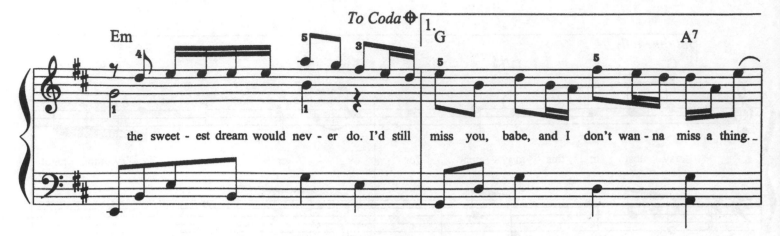

the sweet - est dream would nev - er do. I'd still | miss you, babe, and I don't wan - na miss a thing.

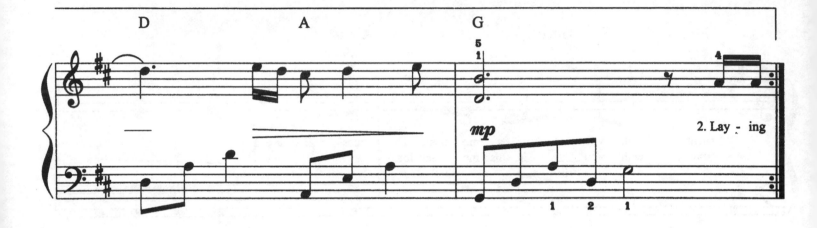

2. Lay - ing

miss you, babe, and I don't wan - na miss a thing._____ I don't wan - na

miss one smile. I don't wan - na miss one kiss. I just wan - na

be with you, right here with you, just like this. I just wan - na

hold you close, feel your heart so close to mine, _____ and just

stay here in this mo - ment for all the rest of time.

D.S. 𝄋 al Coda

Ba - by, ba - by.___

ff

Coda

miss you, babe, and I don't wan - na miss a thing.__

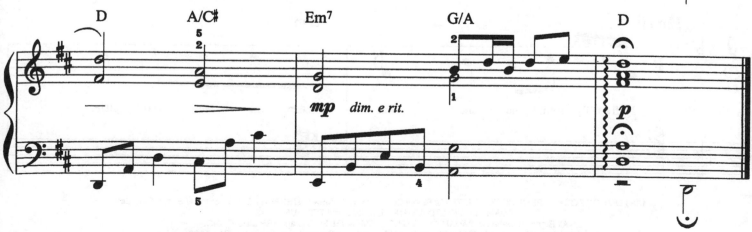

mp *dim. e rit.*

p

From the Motion Picture "THE MIRROR HAS TWO FACES"

I FINALLY FOUND SOMEONE

Written by
BARBRA STREISAND, MARVIN HAMLISCH,
R. J. LANGE and BRYAN ADAMS
Arranged by DAN COATES

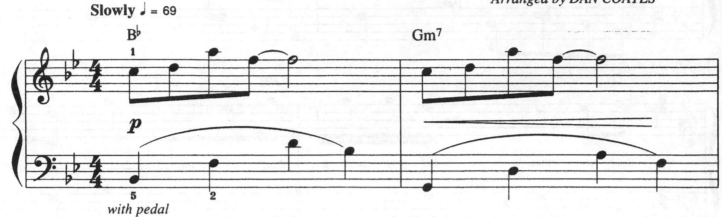

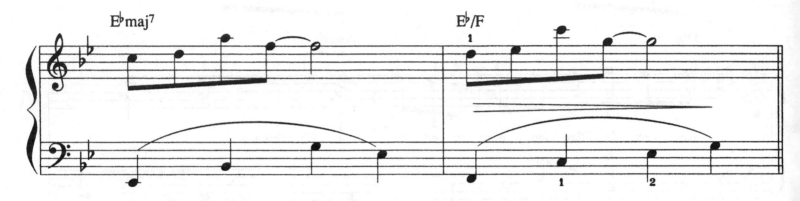

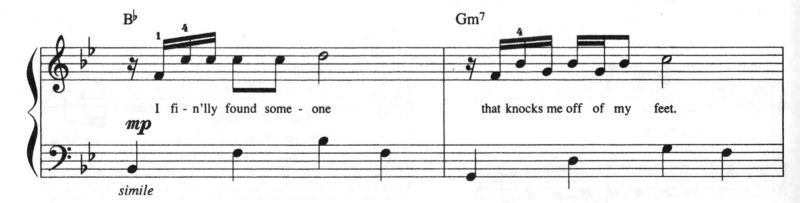

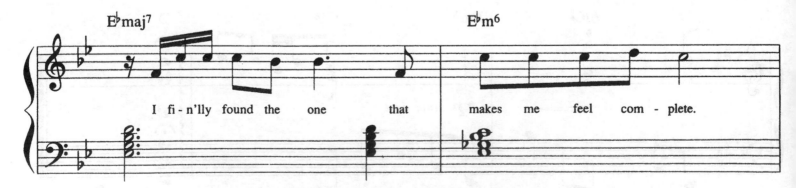

It's all you had to say to take my breathe a - way.

This is it! Oh, I fi - n'lly

found some - one, some - one to share my life. I fi - n'lly

found the one to be with ev - 'ry night. 'Cause what -

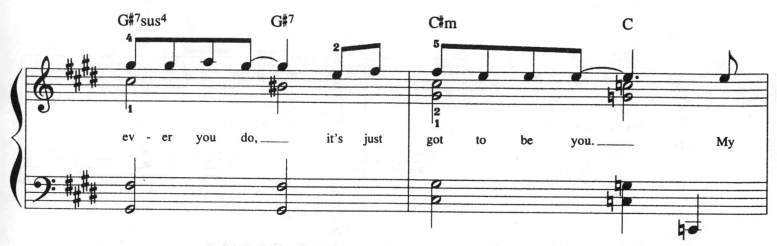

ev - er you do, ___ it's just got to be you. ___ My

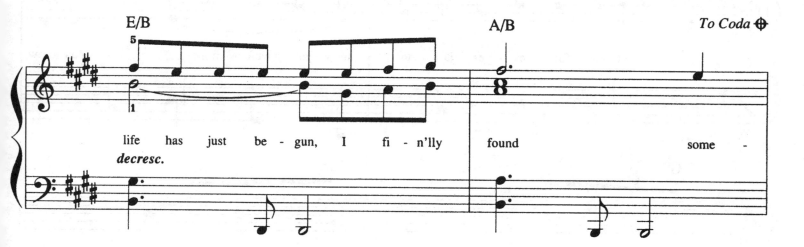

life has just be - gun, I fi - n'lly found some -

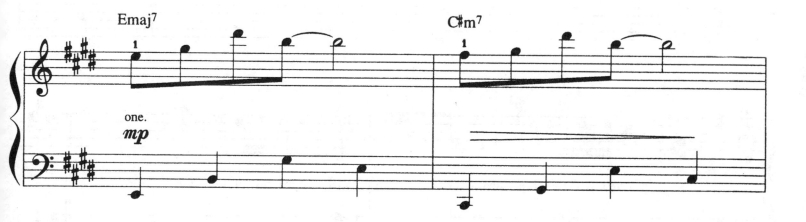

one.

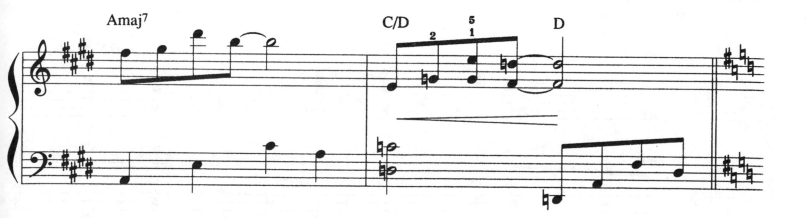

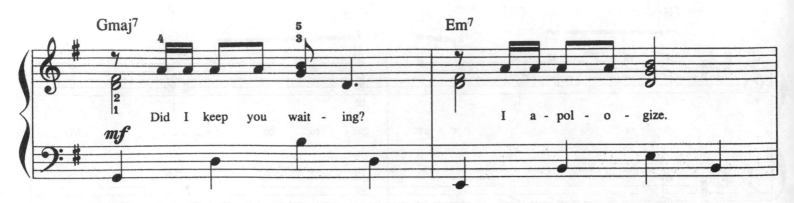

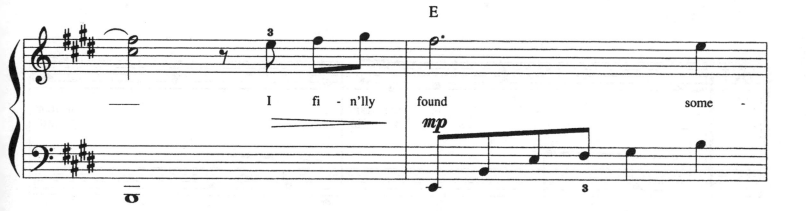

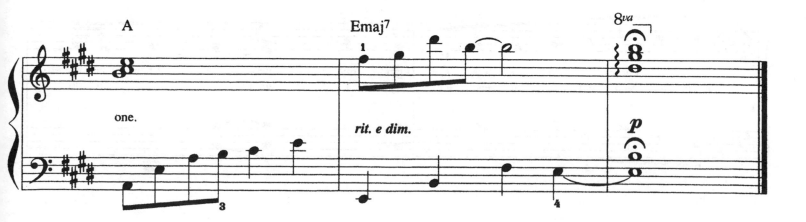

I TURN TO YOU

Words and Music by
DIANE WARREN
Arranged by DAN COATES

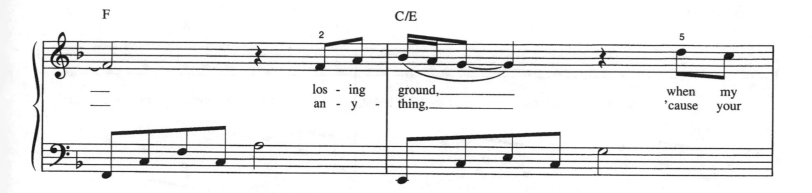

%. *Chorus:*

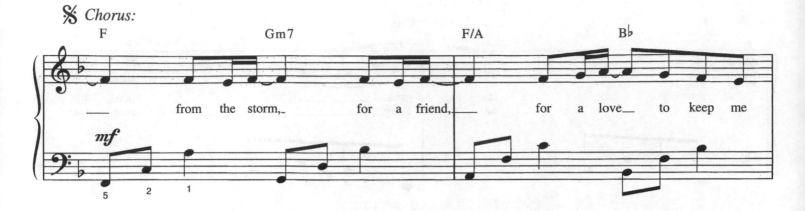

from the storm,_ for a friend,_ for a love_ to keep me

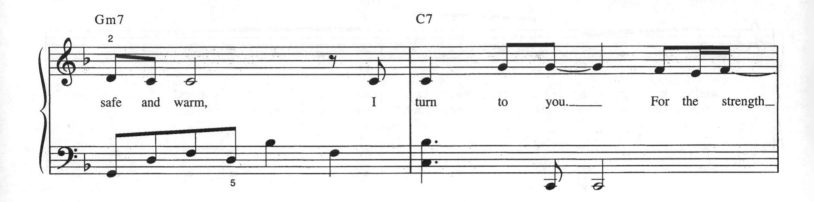

safe and warm, I turn to you._ For the strength_

To Coda ⊕

_ to be strong,_ for the will to car - ry on, for

1.

ev - 'ry-thing_ you do, for ev - 'ry-thing_ that's true, I turn to

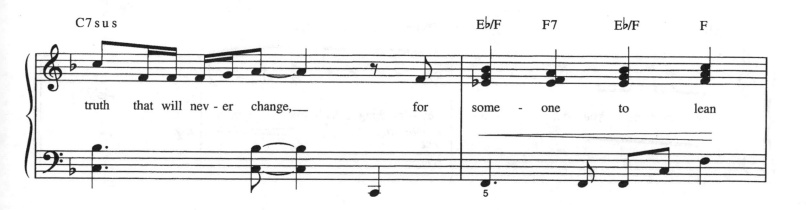

Eb
Bb/D

on, for a heart I can re - ly on through an - y - thing,___ for that

Gm7/C
C7
D.S. 𝄋 al Coda

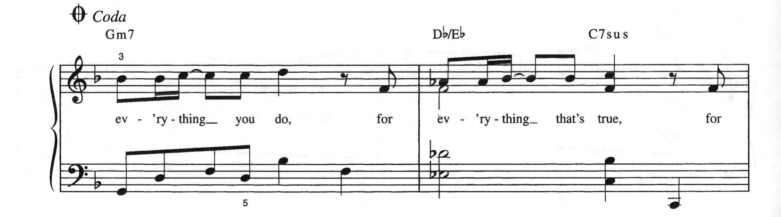

one who___ I can run to. For a shield___

𝄌 *Coda*
Gm7
Db/Eb
C7sus

ev - 'ry - thing___ you do, for ev - 'ry - thing___ that's true, for

Gm7
Db/Eb
C7sus
F

ev - 'ry - thing___ you do, for ev - 'ry - thing___ that's true, I turn to you.

molto rit.
mp

I WANT YOU TO NEED ME

Words and Music by
DIANE WARREN
Arranged by DAN COATES

Slowly, in 2 ♩ = 78

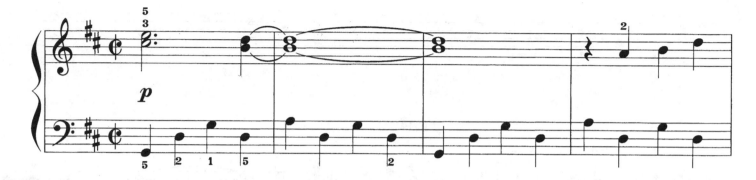

1.3. I wan-na be the face you see__ when you close your eyes. __

2. I wan-na be the eyes that look__ deep in-to your soul. __

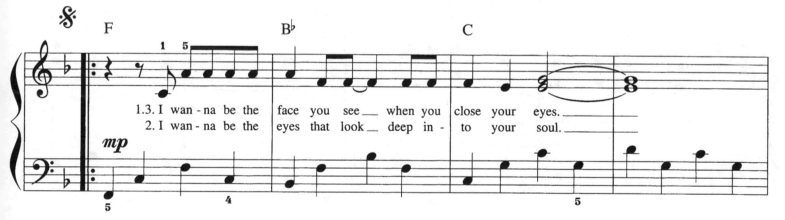

I wan-na be the touch you need__ ev-'ry sin-gle night. __

I wan-na be the world to you. __ I just want it all. __

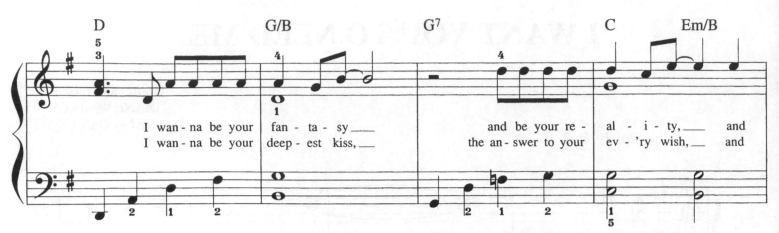

I wan-na be your fan-ta-sy ___ and be your re - al - i - ty, ___ and
I wan-na be your deep-est kiss, ___ the an-swer to your ev-'ry wish, ___ and

ev -'ry - thing ___ be - tween. I want you to need me ___ like the
all you ev - er need. I want you to

air you ___ breathe. I want you to feel me ___ in

ev - 'ry - thing. ___ I want you to see me ___ in your

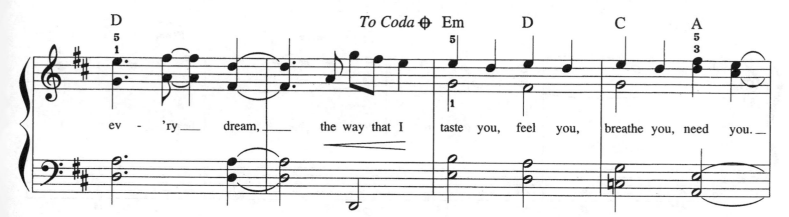

ev - 'ry___ dream,___ the way that I taste you, feel you, breathe you, need you.___

___ I want you to need me like I need you. 'Cause

I need___ you___ more than you___ could know.___ And

I need___ you___ to nev - er, nev - er let___ me go.___ And

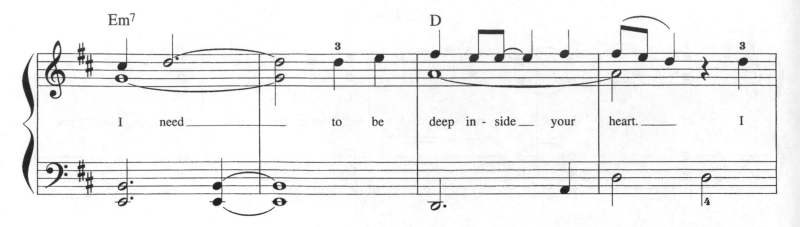

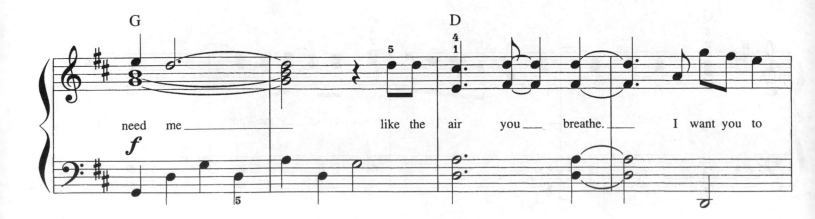

feel me _____ in ev - 'ry - thing. _____ I want you to

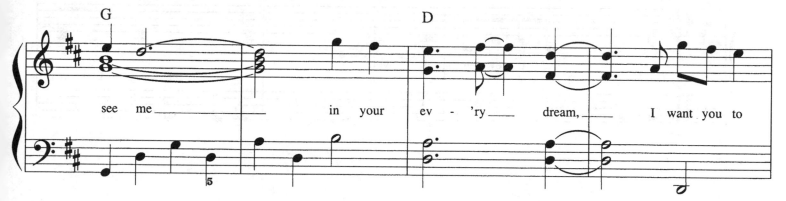

see me _____ in your ev - 'ry _____ dream, _____ I want you to

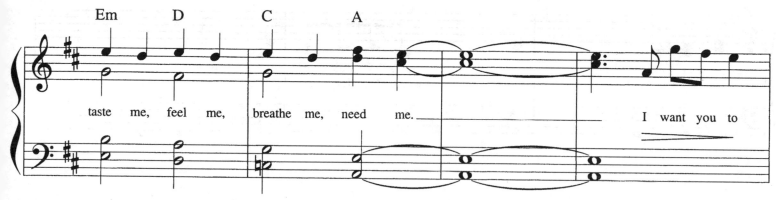

taste me, feel me, breathe me, need me. _____ I want you to

need me _____ like I need you, _____ like I need you, _____

mf   *dim. poco a poco*

like I need you.

mp   *rit.*   *p*

I WILL LOVE AGAIN

Words and Music by
PAUL BARRY and MARK TAYLOR
Arranged by DAN COATES

Moderately fast ($\quarternote$ = 128)

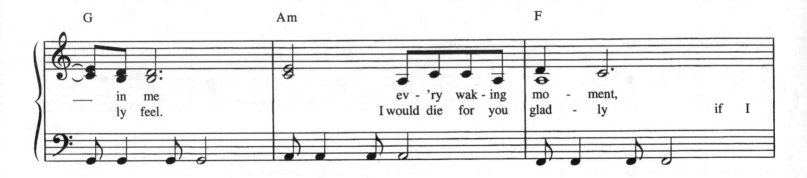

Am   F   C/G   G

mat - ter,_____   just as long as I___ be - lieve?   I will love_
mat - ter_____   if it gets me through_ this night?

Am   F   C/G

_____ a - gain.____   Though my heart___ is break -

G   Am   F

ing, I___ will love a - gain,   strong - er than___ be -

C/G   G   Am   F

fore._____   I will love___ a - gain,___

C/G — G — Am — *To Coda* ⊕

e - ven if it takes a life - time to___ get o - ver you.

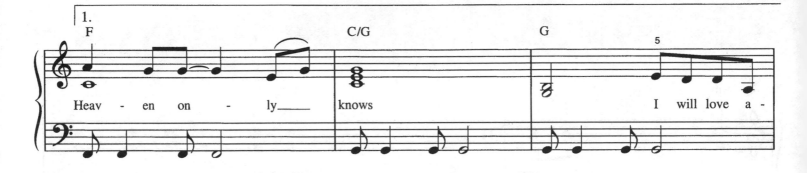

1.

F — C/G — G — 5

Heav - en on - ly___ knows I will love a -

Am

gain.___

2.

F — C/G — G — 1

Heav - en on - ly knows. If I'm

F — Em — Dm — Am

true to my - self, no - bod - y else can take the place of you. But I've

mf

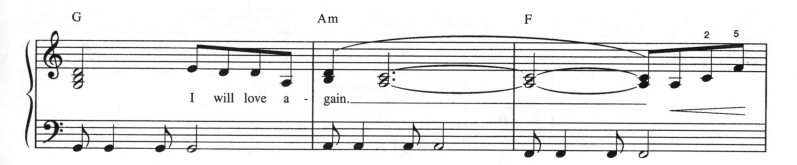

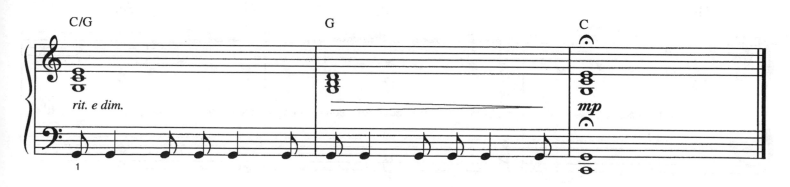

From The Fox Searchlight Film, "THE BROTHERS McMULLEN"

I WILL REMEMBER YOU

Words and Music by
SARAH McLACHLAN, SEAMUS EGAN
and DAVID MERENDA
Arranged by DAN COATES

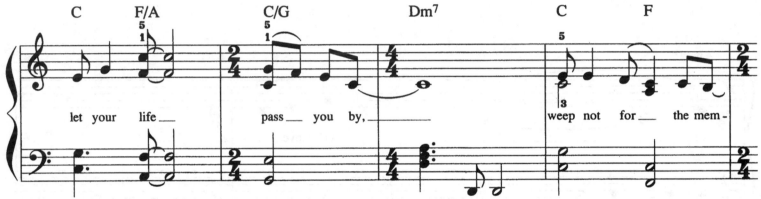

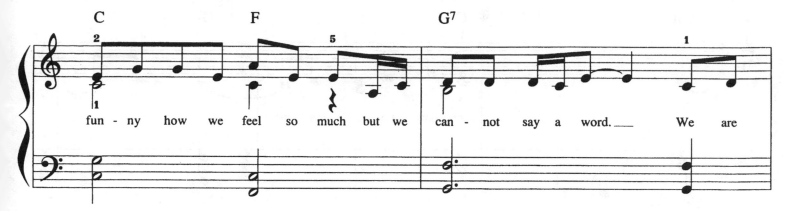

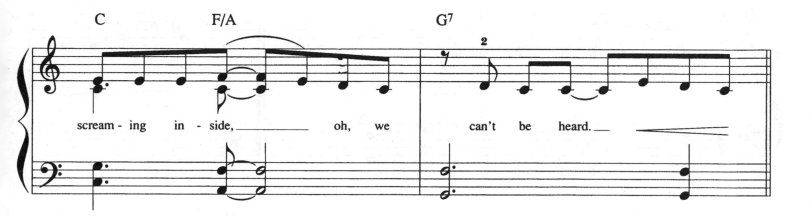

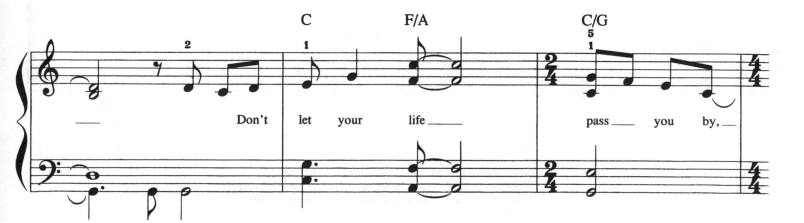

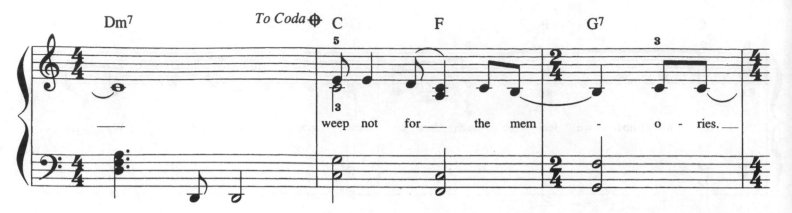

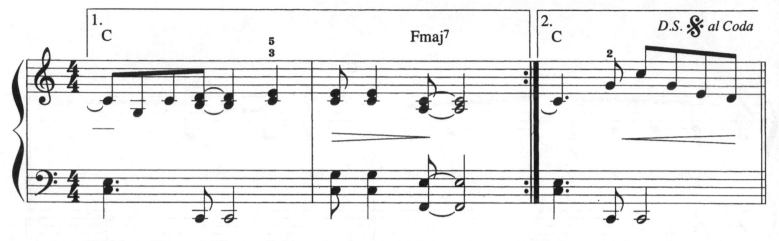

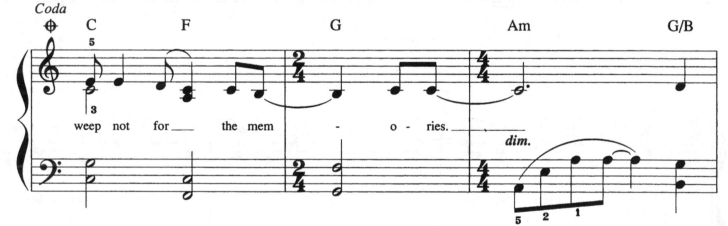

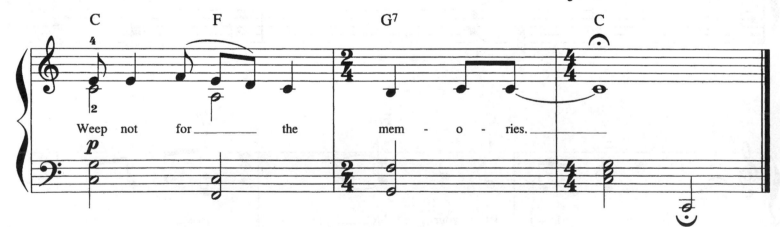

Verse 2:
So afraid to love you, more afraid to lose.
I'm clinging to a past that doesn't let me choose.
Where once there was a darkness, a deep and endless night,
You gave me everything you had, oh, you gave me life.
(To Chorus:)

IN THIS LIFE

Words and Music by
MIKE REID and
ALLEN SHAMBLIN
Arranged by DAN COATES

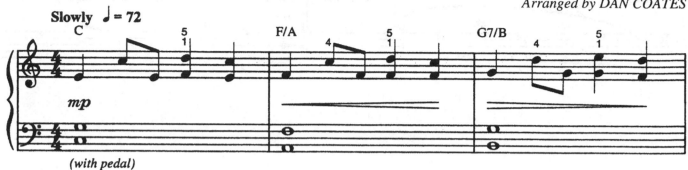

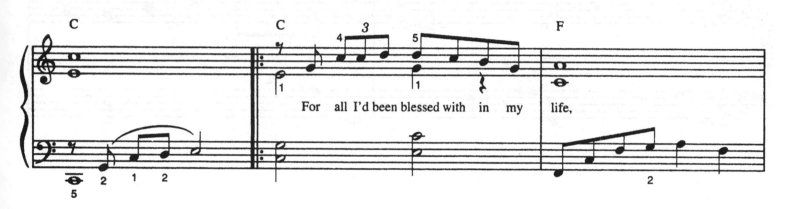

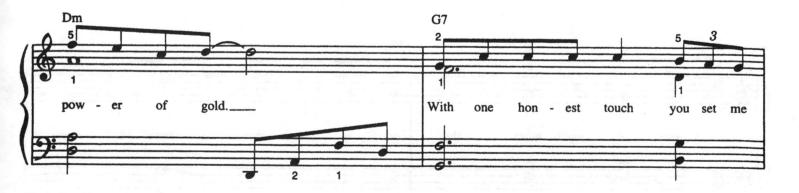

90

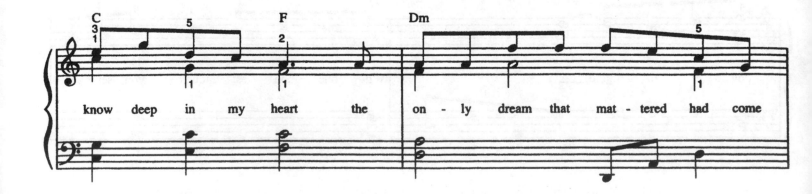

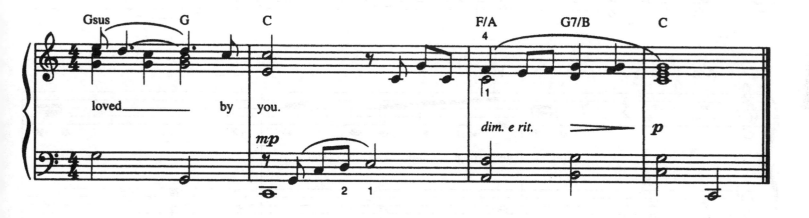

Verse 2:
For every mountain I have climbed,
Every raging river crossed,
You were the treasure that I longed to find.
Without your love I would be lost.
(To Chorus:)

KISS THE RAIN

Words and Music by
ERIC BAZILIAN, DESMOND CHILD
and BILLIE MYERS
Arranged by DAN COATES

Moderately slow ♩ = 92

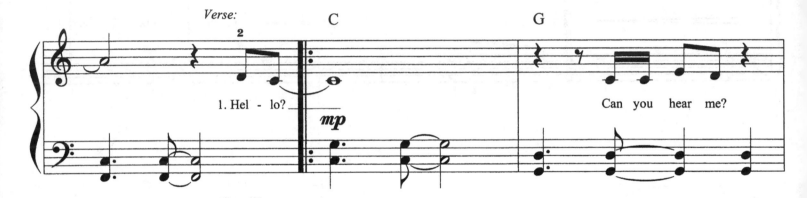

G · Am · G

try - ing to___ ex - plain. Some - thing's wrong,___ you just don't sound___

Am · G · F · *Chorus:*

the same. Why don't you,___ why don't you___ go out - side,___ go out - side? Kiss the rain___

cresc. ___ *mf*

C · C/E · F

when - ev - er you need___ me. Kiss the rain___ when - ev - er I'm gone___

G · C/E

too long.___ If your lips___ feel lone - ly and thirst - y,___ kiss the rain___

and wait for the dawn. Keep in mind we're un - der the same

sky, and the night's as emp - ty for me as for you. If you feel

you can't wait 'til morn - ing, kiss the rain, kiss the rain,

kiss the rain.

Hel - lo?

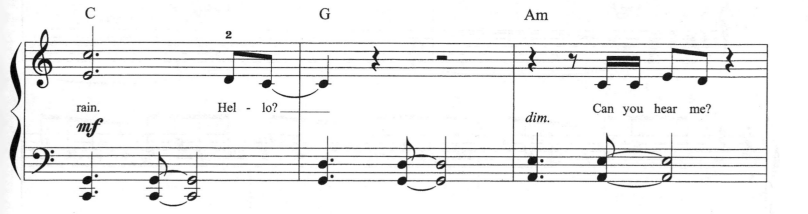

Verse 2:
Hello? Do you miss me?
I hear you say you do,
But not the way I'm missing you.
What's new? How's the weather?
Is it stormy where you are?
You sound so close,
But it feels like you're so far.
Oh, would it mean anything
If you knew what I'm left imagining
In my mind, in my mind.
Would you go, would you go...
(To Chorus:)

LOVE WILL KEEP US ALIVE

Words and Music by
JIM CAPALDI, PETER VALE
and PAUL CARRACK
Arranged by DAN COATES

Moderately slow ♩ = 88

Love Will Keep Us Alive - 4 - 1

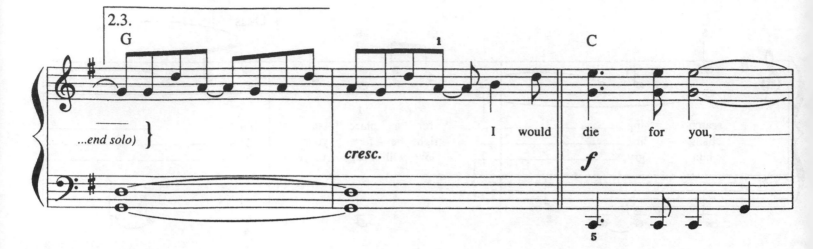

⊕ *Coda*

From the Miramax Motion Picture "Music Of The Heart"

MUSIC OF MY HEART

Words and Music by
DIANE WARREN
Arranged by DAN COATES

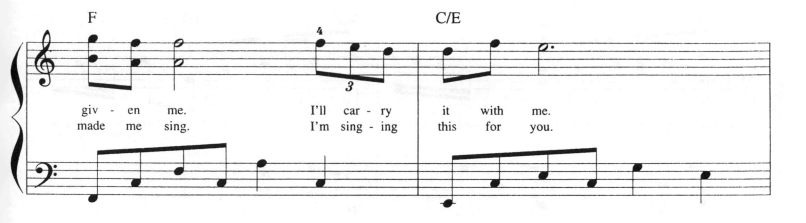

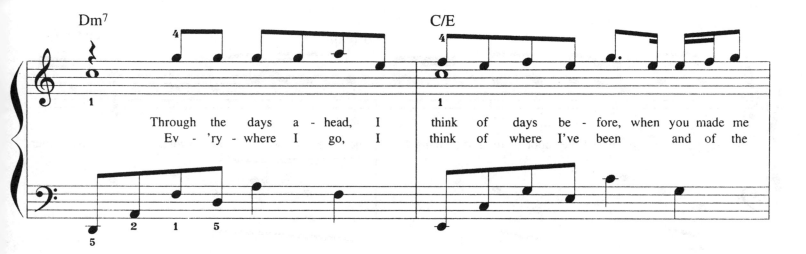

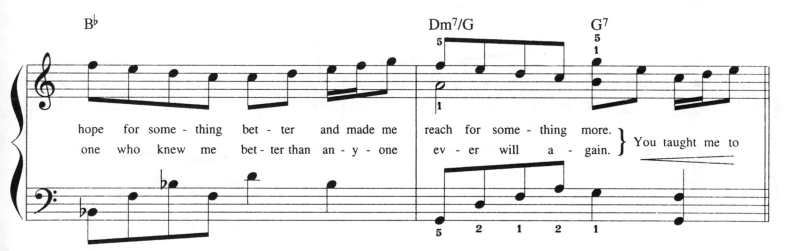

mu - sic of ___ my heart. Helped me hear the mu - sic of ___ my heart. You o - pened my

eyes, you o - pened the door to some - thing I've nev - er known ___ be - fore. And your

To Coda

1.

love _____ is the mu - sic of ___ my heart.

mp

2.

love _____ is the mu - sic of ___ my heart. What you taught __ me, on - ly

mp   *mf*

MENTAL PICTURE

Words and Music by
JON SECADA and
MIGUEL A. MOREJON
Arranged by DAN COATES

1. I've been a- void- ing things I'm miss- ing. Then you

came in- to my life a brand new flow- er. —— Ba- by, ——

a re- mind- er of what hap- pi- ness is like —— on the

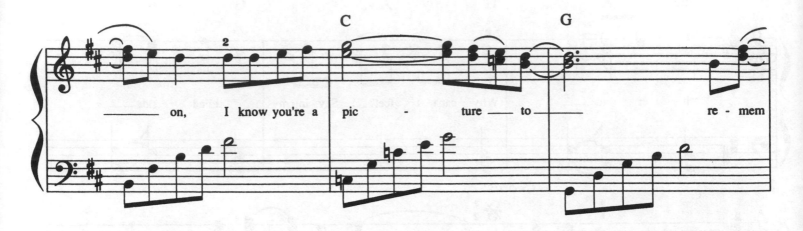

on, I know you're a pic - ture — to — re - mem

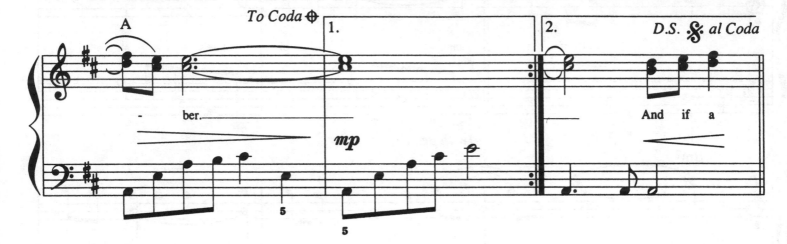

- ber.

mp

And if a

mp

rit.

p

Verse 2:
Time was of the essence,
And as usual the day turns into minutes.
Sharing love and tenderness,
That's the nerve you struck in me that sent a signal.
To the other side,
(Girl, I don't know)
Saying my blind side.
And if a ... *(To Chorus:)*

MY ONE TRUE FRIEND

(From "ONE TRUE THING")

Words and Music by
CAROLE BAYER SAGER, CAROLE KING
and DAVID FOSTER
Arranged by DAN COATES

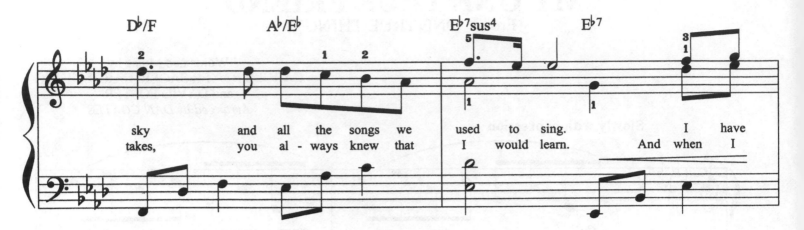

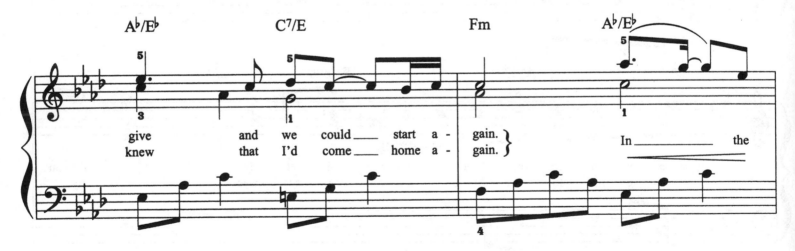

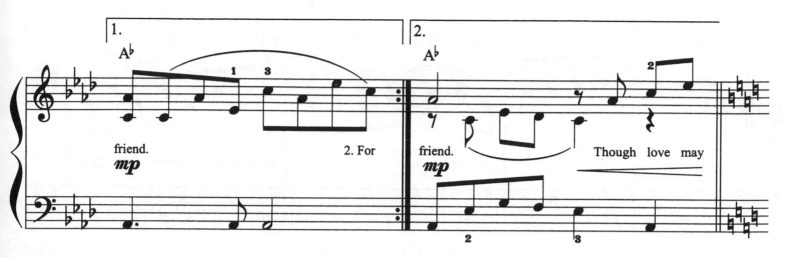

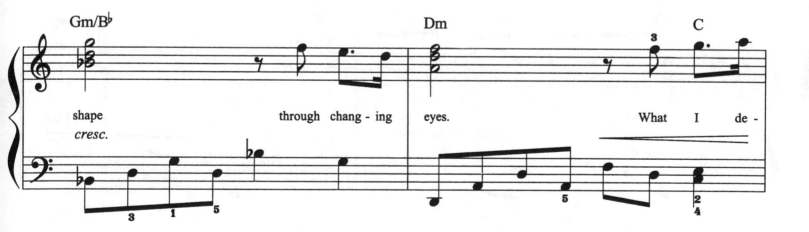

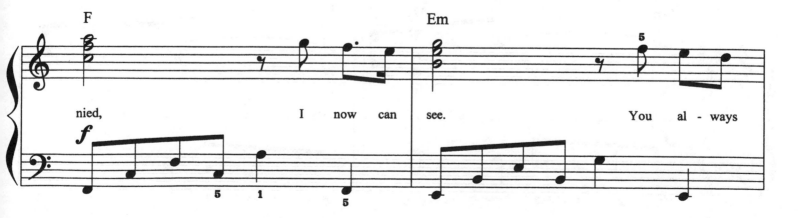

were the light in - side of me.

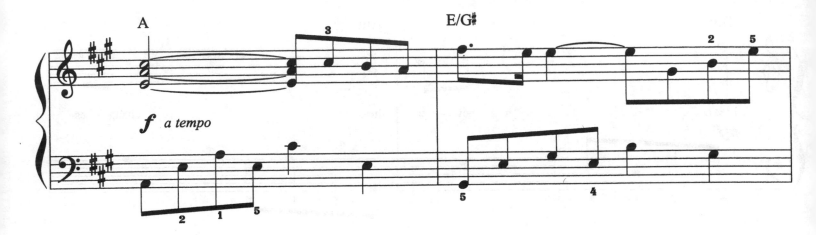

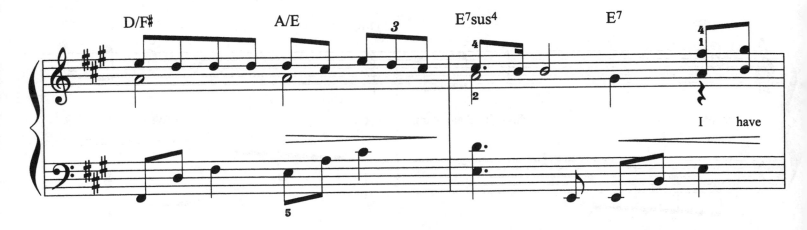

I have

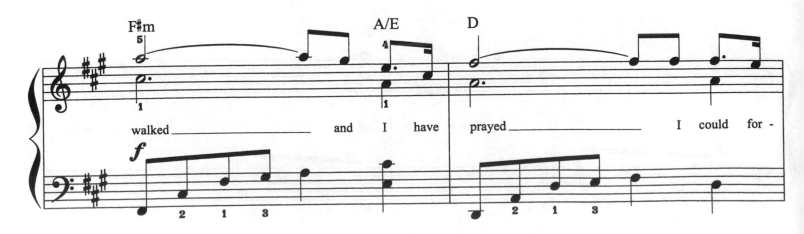

walked and I have prayed I could for -

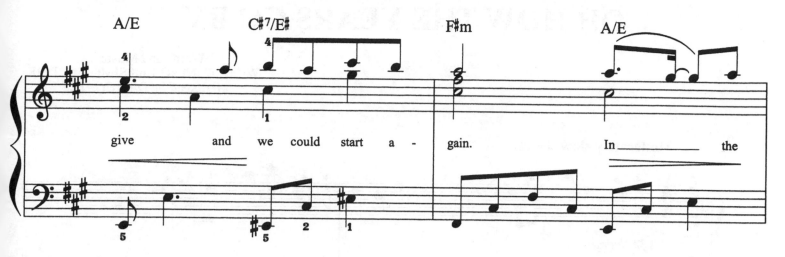

OH HOW THE YEARS GO BY

Words and Music by
WILL JENNINGS anf SIMON CLIMIE
Arranged by DAN COATES

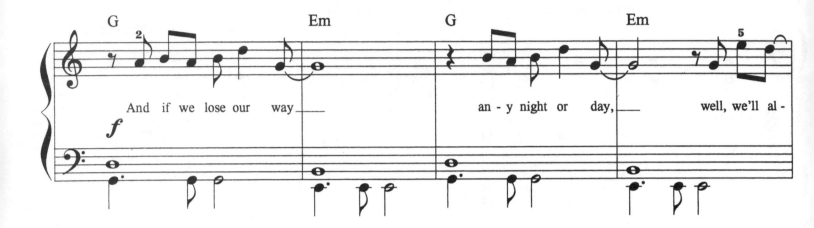

And if we lose our way ____ an - y night or day, ____ well, we'll al-

ways be ____ where we ____ should be. ____ I'm there ____ for you, ____ and I know ____

____ you're ____ there ____ for me. As the years go by. ____

You know you're not a - lone in this world of

stran - gers.

D.S. 𝄋 al Coda

Coda

by. ____

dim.

Oh, how the years go by. ____

mp

Verse 2:
There were times we stumbled,
They thought they had us down,
We came around.
How we rolled and rambled,
We got lost and we got found.
Now we're back on solid ground.
We took everything
All our times would bring
In this world of danger.
'Cause when your heart is strong,
You know you're not alone
In this world of strangers.
(To Chorus:)

NOW AND FOREVER

Music and Lyrics by
RICHARD MARX
Arranged by DAN COATES

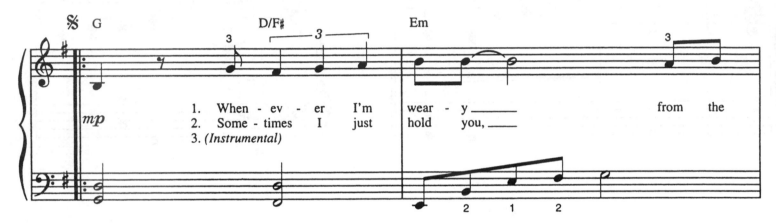

1. When - ev - er I'm wear - y _____ from the
2. Some - times I just hold you, _____
3. *(Instrumental)*

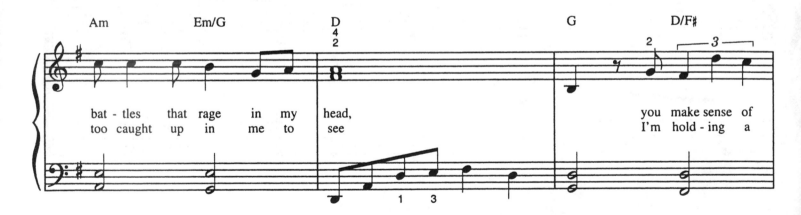

bat - tles that rage in my head, you make sense of
too caught up in me to see I'm hold - ing a

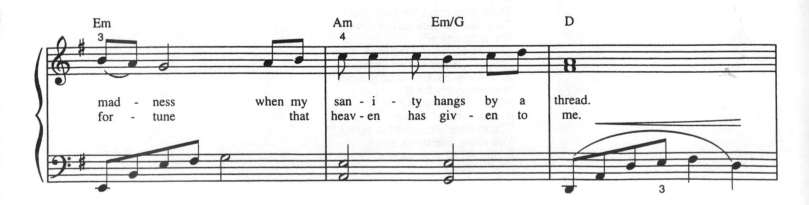

mad - ness when my san - i - ty hangs by a thread.
for - tune that heav - en has giv - en to me.

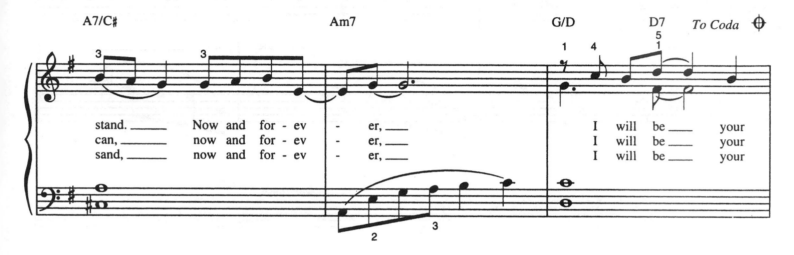

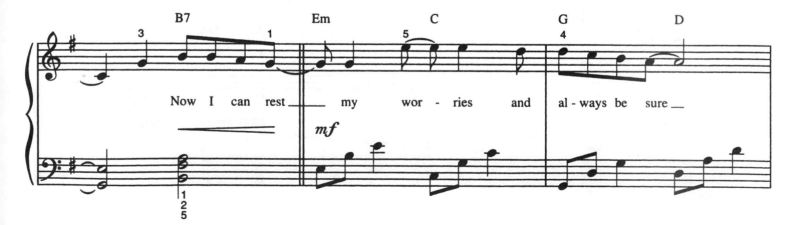

that I won't be a-lone__ an-y-more.__ If I'd on-ly known__

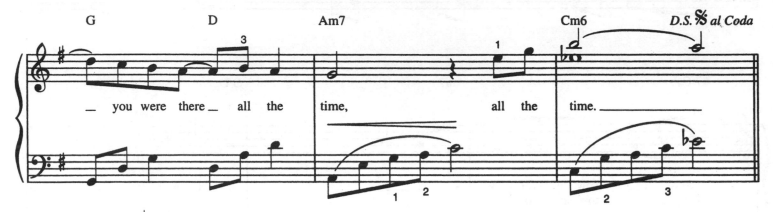

__ you were there __ all the time, all the time._____

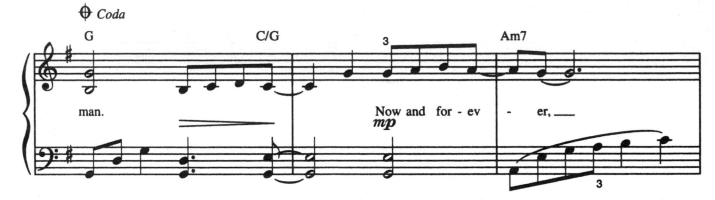

man. Now and for-ev - er, ___

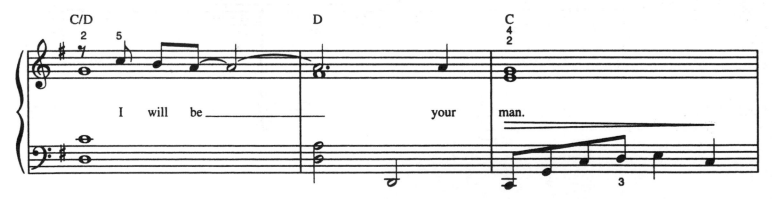

I will be _____ your man.

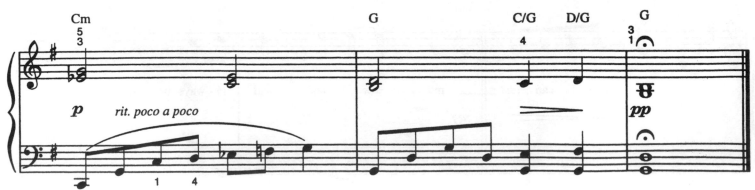

ON MY OWN

Words and Music by
CAROLE BAYER SAGER and BURT BACHARACH
Arranged by DAN COATES

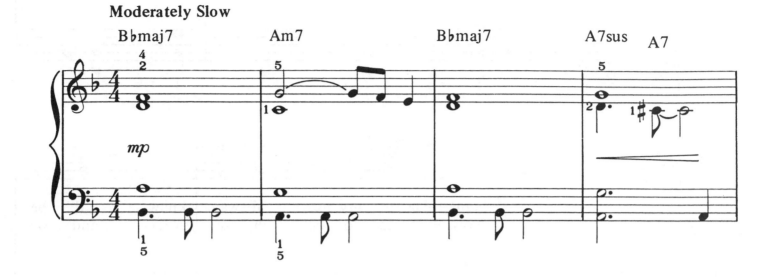

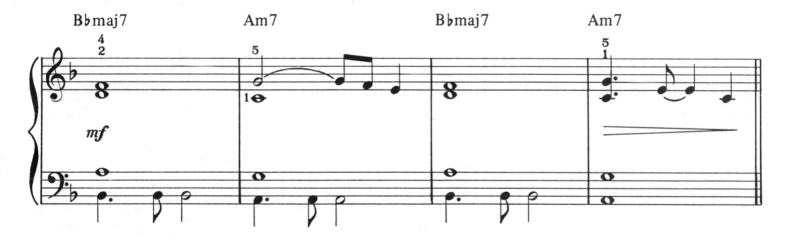

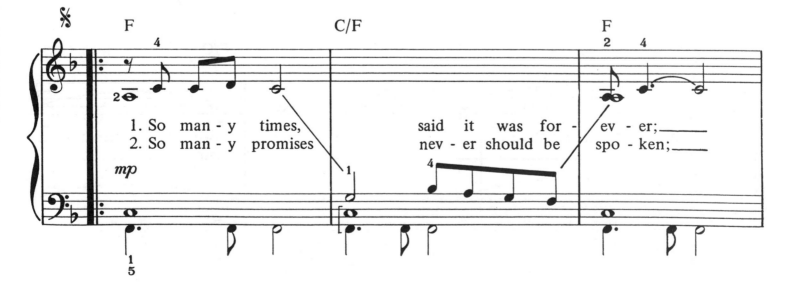

1. So man-y times, said it was for - ev - er;____
2. So man-y promises nev - er should be spo - ken;____

C/F   Bbmaj7   Bb6

said our love would al - ways be true.___
now I know what lov - ing you cost.___

Bbmaj7   Bb6

Some-thing in my heart al - ways knew I'd be
Now we're up to talk - in' di - vorce and we

F/C   *To Coda* ⊕

ly - ing here be - side you.___
were - n't e - ven mar - ried.___   On my
    On my

Gm/C   F/C

own,___   on my own,___
own,___   once a - gain,___

mf

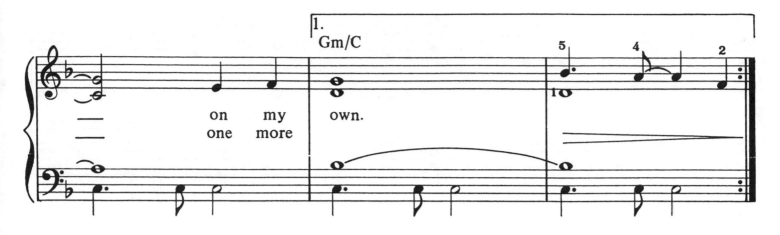

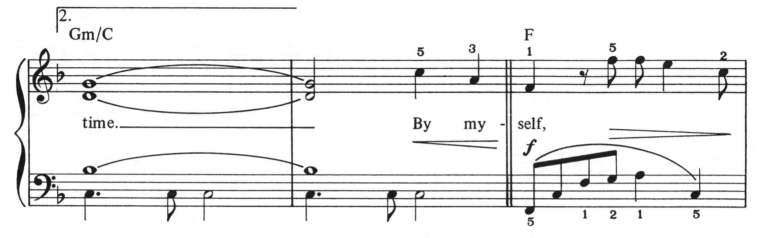

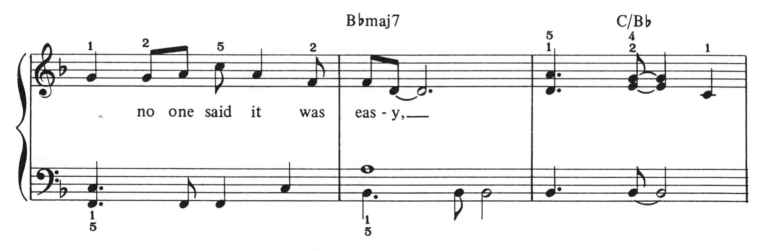

Well, I be - lieved ___ in love, ___ now here ___

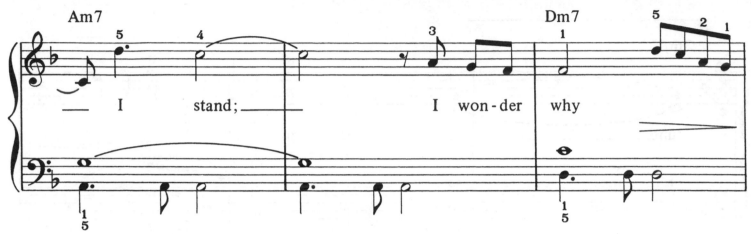

___ I stand; ___ I won-der why

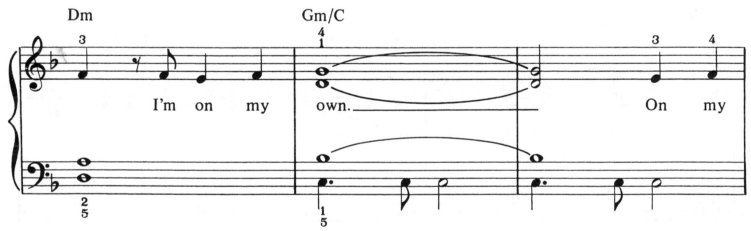

I'm on my own. ___ On my

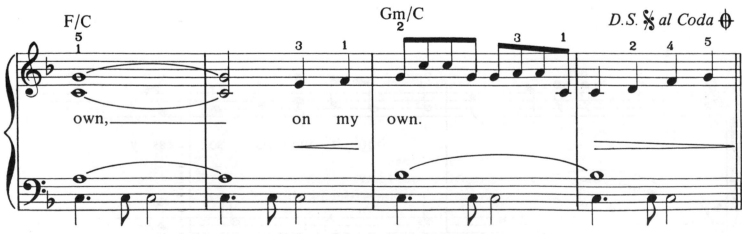

own, ___ on my own.

123

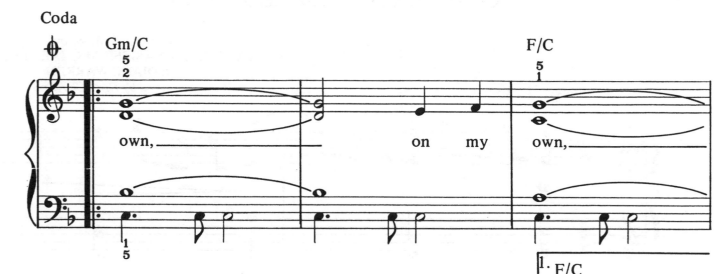

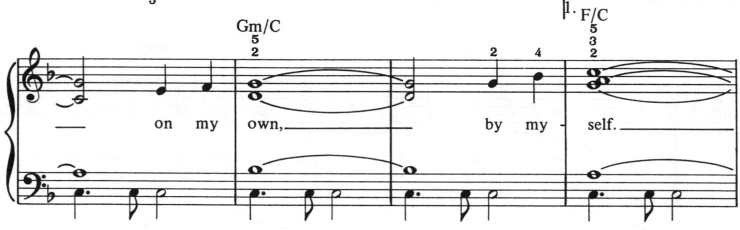

Extra Lyrics:

3. So many times
   I know I could have told you;
   Losin' you, it cuts like a knife.
   You walked out and there went my life;
   I don't want to live without you.
   On my own, *etc.*

From the TriStar Pictures Feature Film "ONLY YOU"

ONCE IN A LIFETIME

Words and Music by
WALTER AFANASIEFF, MICHAEL BOLTON
and DIANE WARREN
Arranged by DAN COATES

125

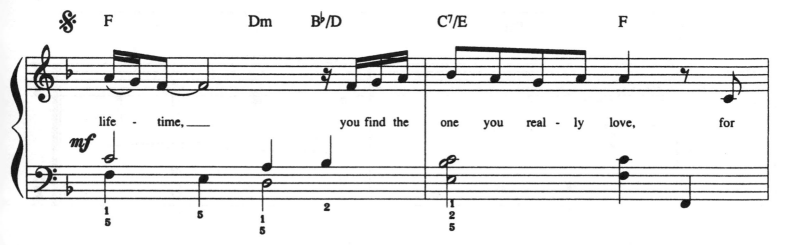

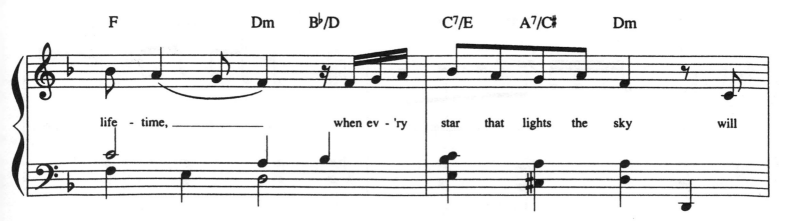

To Coda ⊕

shine with one rea - son, lead - ing your heart to the one love you find, just once in a

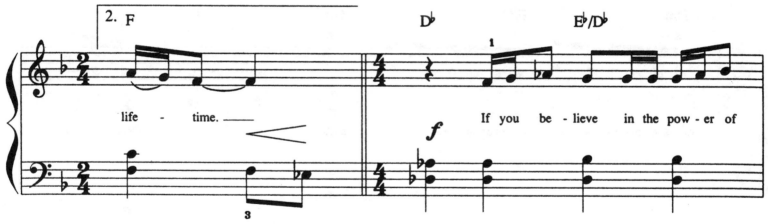

1. life - time. ___

2. life - time. ___ If you be - lieve in the pow - er of

love, ___ then you be - lieve that dreams come true. Mag - ic will fill your heart when that

mo - ment comes a - long   just once in your   life.

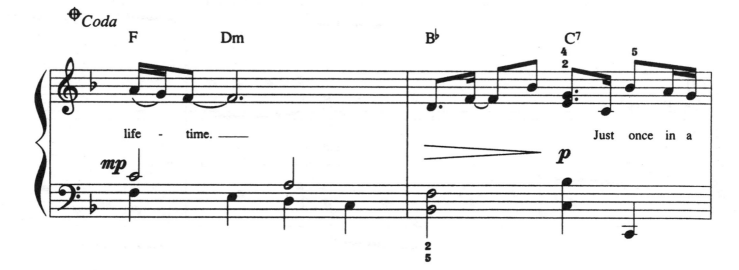

D.S. 𝄋 al Coda

Once in a

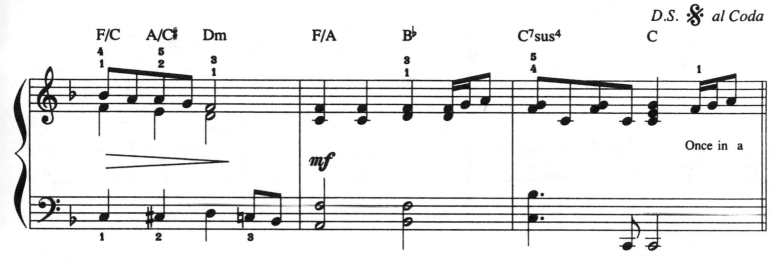

Coda

life - time. ____

Just once in a

life - time. ____

dim. e rit.

THE PRAYER

Words and Music by
CAROLE BAYER SAGER and DAVID FOSTER
Arranged by DAN COATES

129

SAVE THE BEST FOR LAST

Words and Music by
WENDY WALDMAN, JON LIND
and PHIL GALDSTON
Arranged by DAN COATES

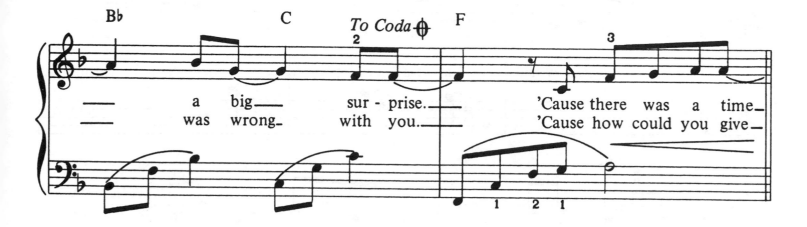

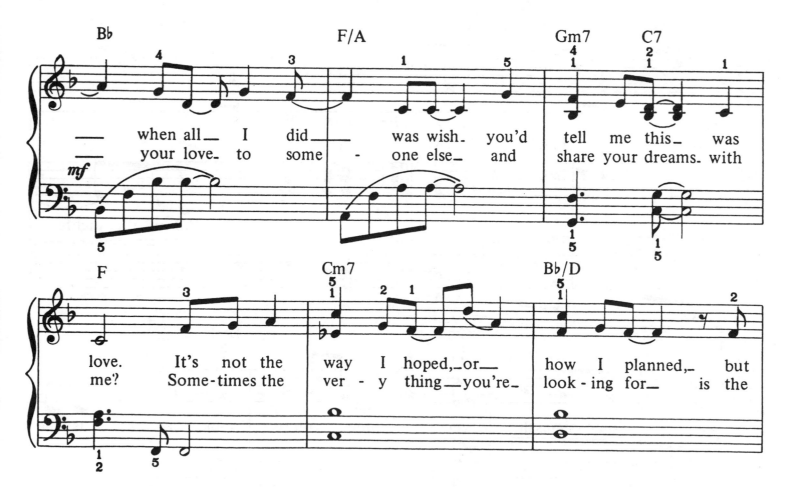

qui - ta, my Span-ish Har-lem Mo - na Lis - a.

You're my rea - son for rea - son, the step in my

groove. And if you said___ this life ain't

good e - nough,___ I would give___ my world to lift you up.___ I could change___

___ my life to bet - ter suit___ your___ mood.

'Cause you're so smooth. Oh, and it's

Chorus:

just like the o - cean un - der the moon.__ Well, it's the same as the e - mo - tion that I

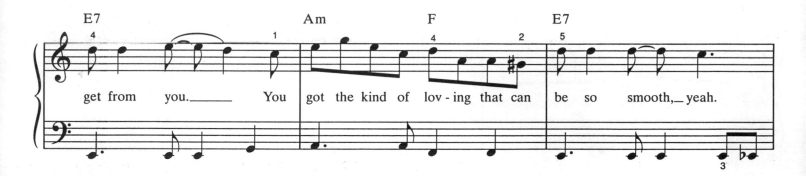

get from you._____ You got the kind of lov - ing that can be so smooth,__ yeah.

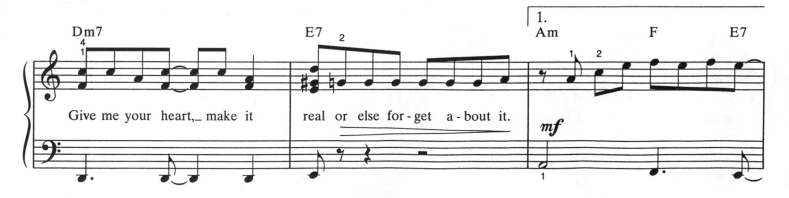

Give me your heart,__ make it real or else for - get a - bout it.

1.

2. Well, I'll tell you

Verse 2:
Well, I'll tell you one thing,
If you should leave, it'd be a crying shame.
In every breath and every word
I hear your name calling me out, yeah.
Well, out from the barrio,
You hear my rhythm on your radio.
You feel the tugging of the world,
So soft and slow, turning you 'round and 'round.
And if you said this life ain't good enough,
I would give my world to lift you up.
I could change my life to better suit your mood.
'Cause you're so smooth.
(To Chorus:)

SOMETHING ABOUT THE WAY YOU LOOK TONIGHT

Lyrics by
BERNIE TAUPIN

Music by
ELTON JOHN
Arranged by DAN COATES

Moderately slow ♩ = 72

Something About the Way You Look Tonight - 3 - 1

scribe, _____ but it's some-thing a-bout the way you look to-night.

It takes my breath a-way, _____ *dim.* the way you look to-

1. night. *mp* With you

2. night.

The way you look to-night. _____ The way you look to-night. _____ The way you

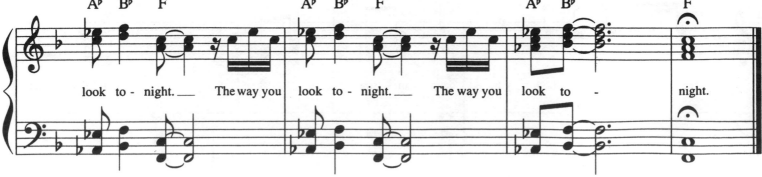

look to-night. _____ The way you look to-night. _____ The way you look to- night.

THE SWEETEST DAYS

Words and Music by
WENDY WALDMAN, JON LIND
and PHIL GALDSTON
Arranged by DAN COATES

Slowly ♩ = 78

p legato

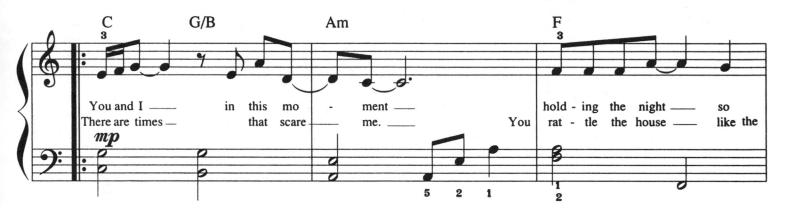

You and I _____ in this mo - ment _____ hold - ing the night _____ so
There are times _____ that scare me. _____ You rat - tle the house _____ like the

close; _____ hang - in' on, _____ still un - bro - ken, while
wind. _____ Both of us _____ so un - bend - ing, we

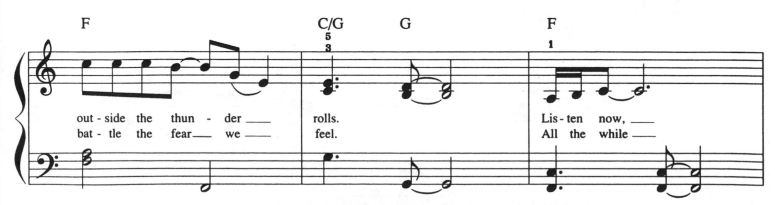

out - side the thun - der _____ rolls. Lis - ten now, _____
bat - tle the fear _____ we _____ feel. All the while _____

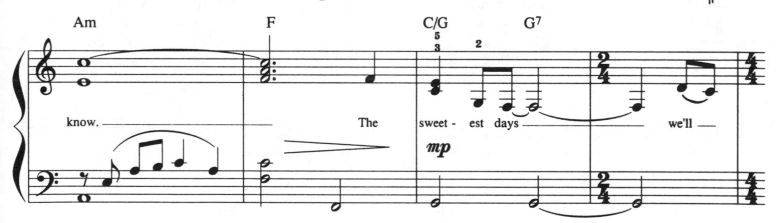

TAKE A BOW

Words and Music by
MADONNA CICCONE and BABYFACE
Arranged by DAN COATES

Moderate calypso feel ♩ = 80

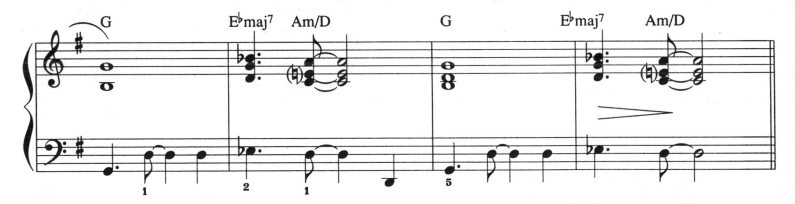

Take a bow,___ the night is o - ver, this mas-que-rade___ is

Make them laugh,___ it comes so eas - y when you get to the part___ where you're

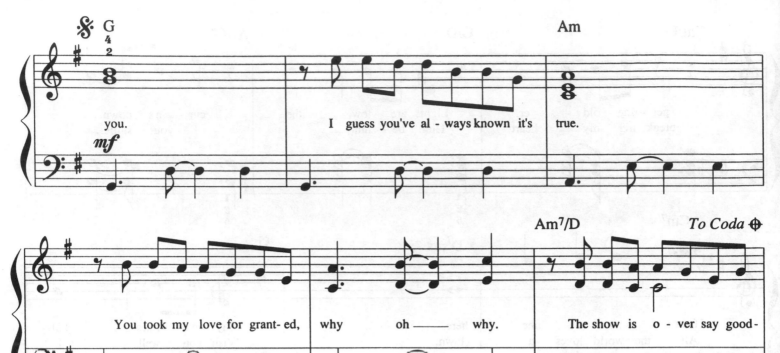

you.

I guess you've al-ways known it's true.

You took my love for grant-ed, why oh ——— why. The show is o-ver say good-

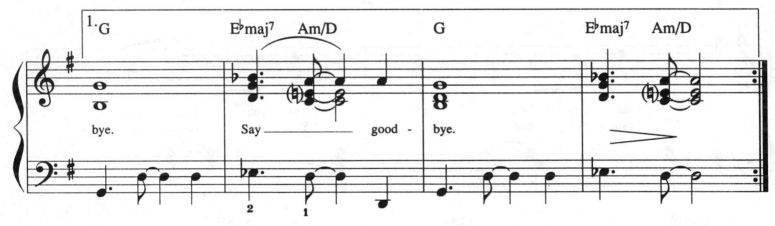

bye. Say ——— good - bye.

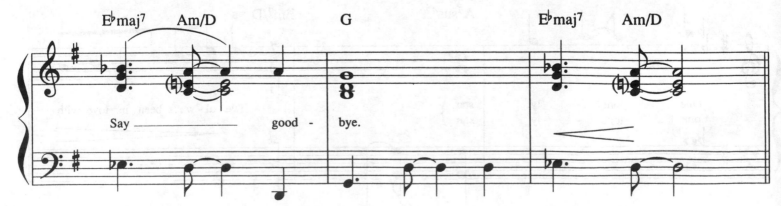

bye. I've al-ways been in love with bye.

Say ——— good - bye.

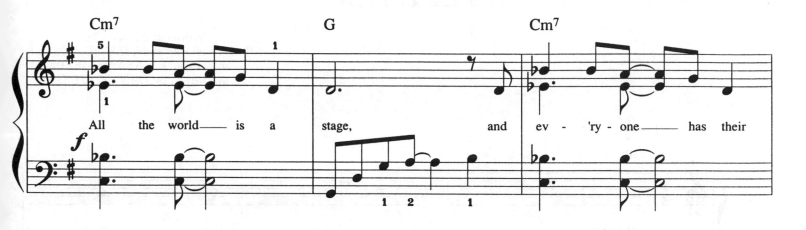

All the world—— is a stage, and ev-'ry-one—— has their

part. But how was I —— to know which way the sto-ry'd go.

How was I to know you'd break, you'd break, you'd break, you'd break, you'd break my heart? I've al-ways been in love with

bye. Say —— good-bye.

TELL HIM

Words and Music by
LINDA THOMPSON, DAVID FOSTER
and WALTER AFANASIEFF
Arranged by DAN COATES

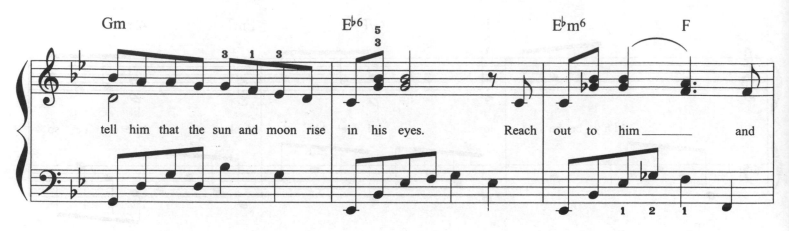

tell him that the sun and moon rise in his eyes. Reach out to him ____ and

whis - per tender words so soft and sweet. I'll hold him close to feel his heart beat.

Barbra: Love will be the gift you give your - self.

self. *Celine:* Love is light that sure - ly glows in the hearts of those who

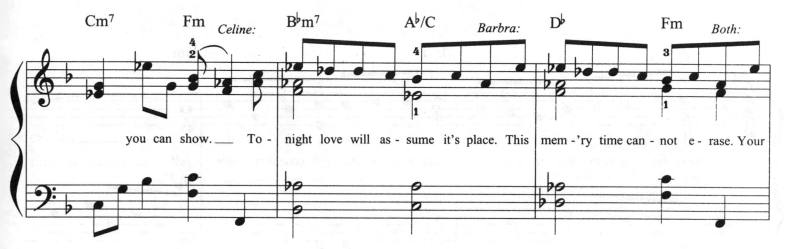

152

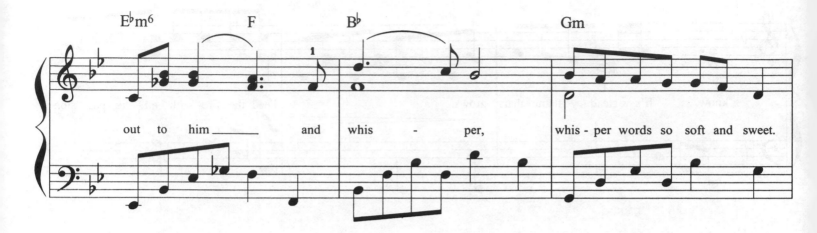

out to him _____ and whis - per, whisp - per words so soft and sweet.

Hold him close to feel his heart beat. Love will be the gift you give your - self. _____
dim. *mf*

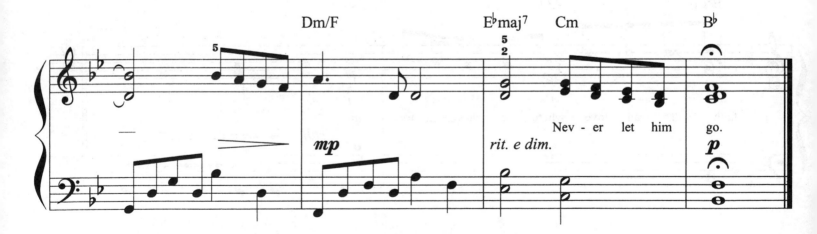

Nev - er let him go.
rit. e dim. *p*

Verse 2:
(Barbra:)
Touch him with the gentleness you feel inside.
Your love can't be denied.
The truth will set you free.
You'll have what's meant to be.
All in time, you'll see.
(Celine:)
I love him,
Of that much I can be sure.
I don't think I could endure
If I let him walk away
When I have so much to say.
(To Chorus:)

TOO LATE, TOO SOON

Words and Music by
JON SECADA, JAMES HARRIS III
and TERRY LEWIS
Arranged by DAN COATES

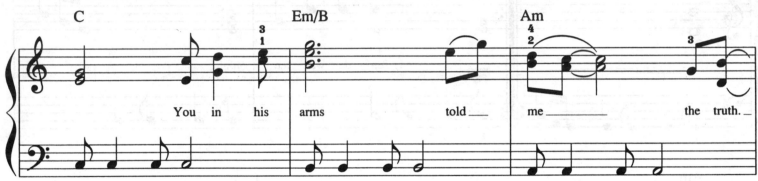

UN-BREAK MY HEART

Words and Music by
DIANE WARREN
Arranged by DAN COATES

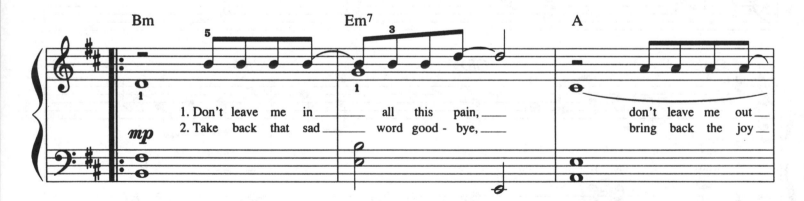

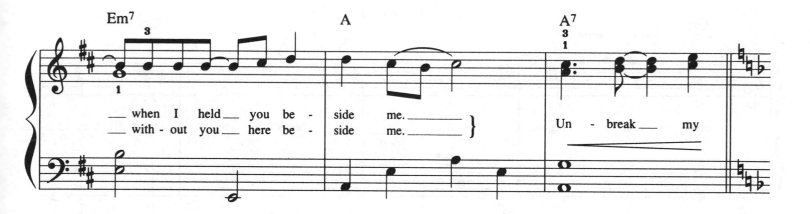

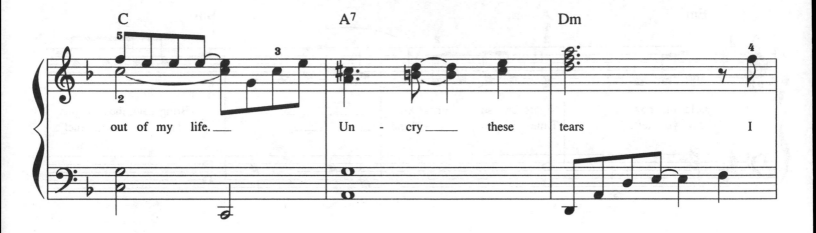

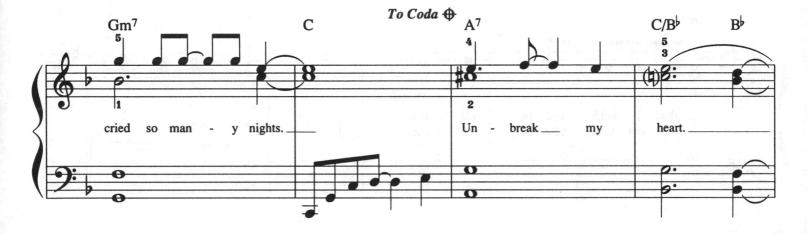

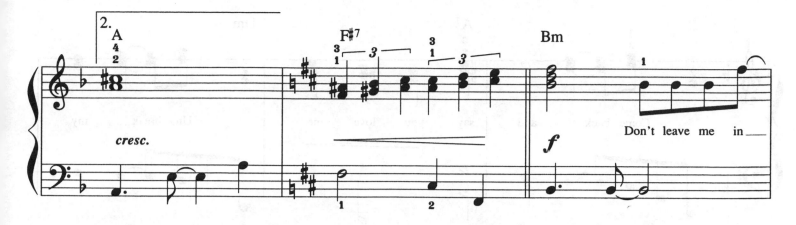

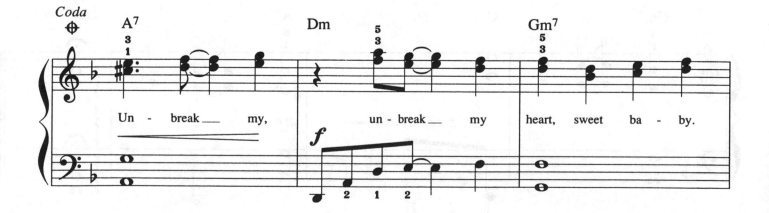

Come back___ and say you love me. Un - break___ my

heart, sweet dar - ling. With - out you, I just can't go on.___

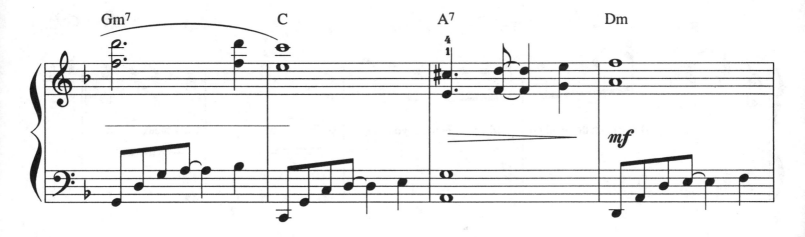

YOU WERE MEANT FOR ME

Words and Music by
JEWEL KILCHER and STEVE POLTZ
Arranged by DAN COATES

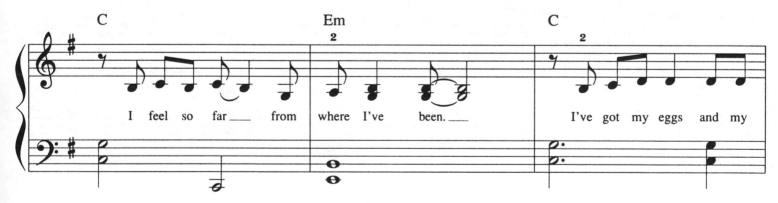

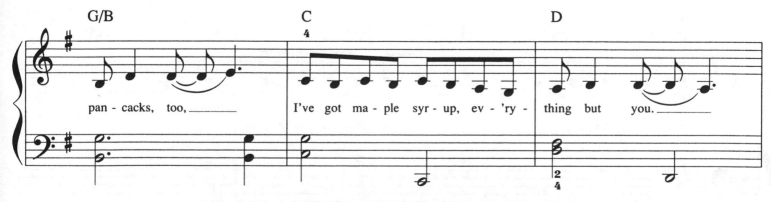

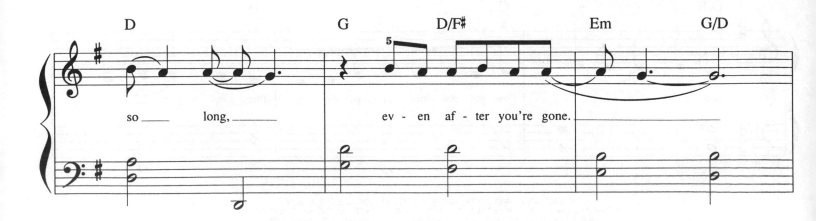

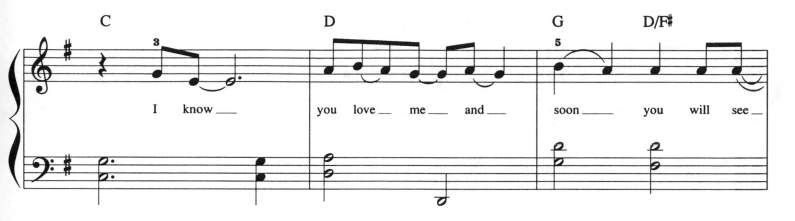

I know ___ you love ___ me ___ and ___ soon ___ you will see ___

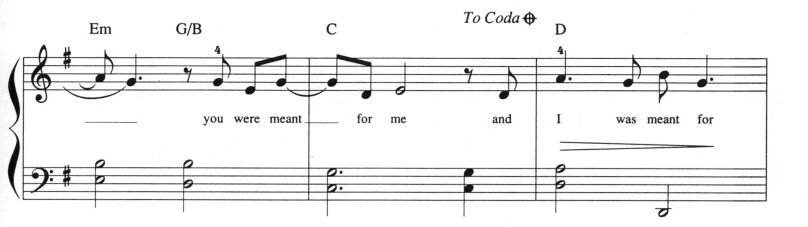

To Coda ⊕

___ you were meant ___ for me and I was meant for

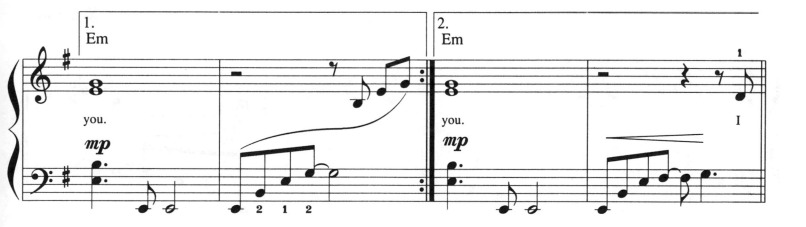

1.
you.

2.
you.

I

go a - bout my bus - 'ness, I'm do - in' fine. ___ Be - sides, ___ what would I say ___ if I had ___

you on the line? Same old sto - ry, not much to say.

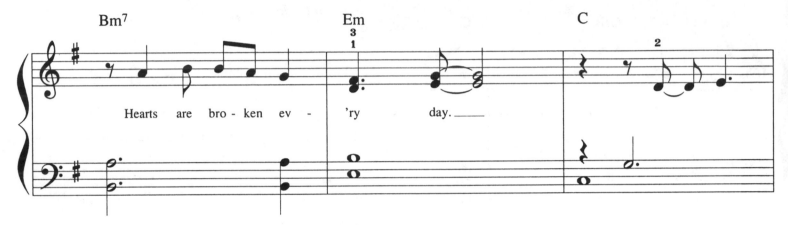

Hearts are bro - ken ev - 'ry day. ___

D.S. 𝄋 *al Coda*

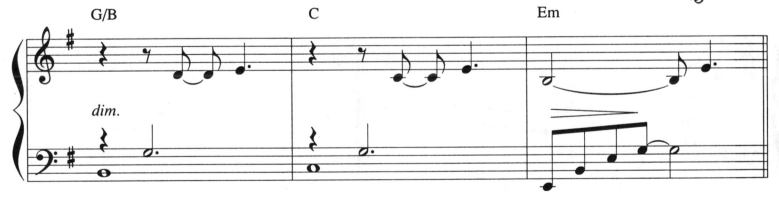

dim.

Coda

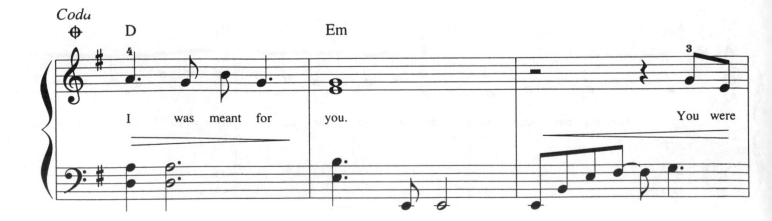

I was meant for you. You were

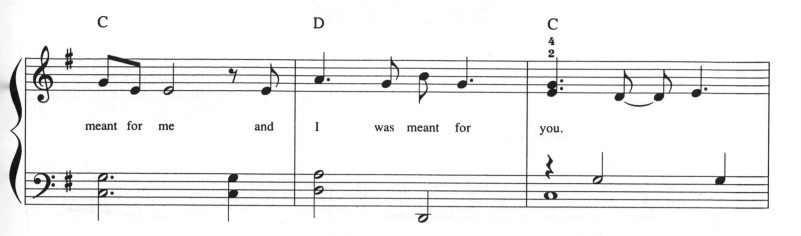

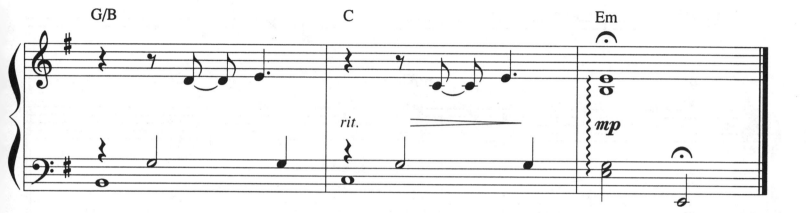

Verse 2:
I called my mama, she was out for a walk.
Consoled a cup of coffee, but it didn't wanna talk.
So I picked up a paper, it was more bad news,
More hearts being broken or people being used.
Put on my coat in the pouring rain.
I saw a movie, it just wasn't the same,
'Cause it was happy and I was sad,
And it made me miss you, oh, so bad.
(To Chorus:)

Verse 3:
I brush my teeth and put the cap back on,
I know you hate it when I leave the light on.
I pick a book up and then I turn the sheets down,
And then I take a breath and a good look around.
Put on my pj's and hop into bed.
I'm half alive but I feel mostly dead.
I try and tell myself it'll be all right,
I just shouldn't think anymore tonight.
(To Chorus:)

VALENTINE

Composed by
JIM BRICKMAN and **JACK KUGELL**
Arranged by DAN COATES

Moderately slow (♩ = 92)

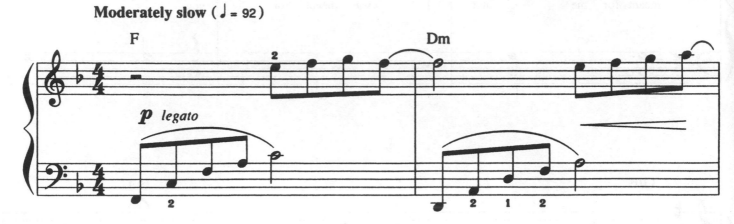

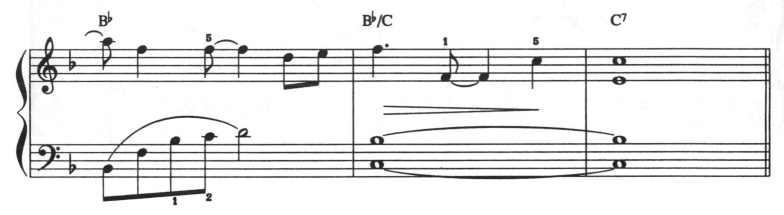

1. If there were no words,___ no way to speak,___

I would still ___ hear ___ you. If there were no tears, ___ no way to feel ___

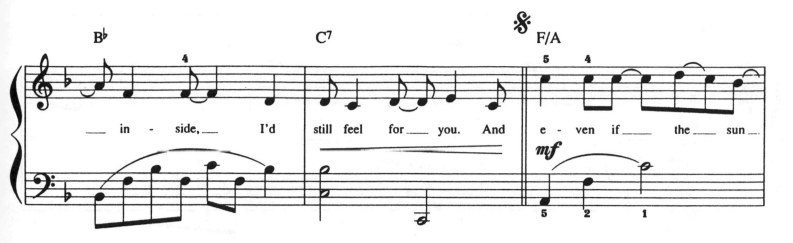

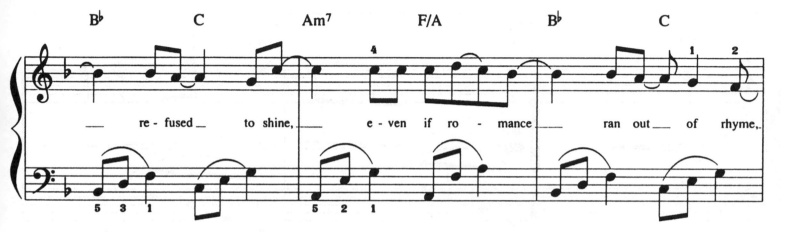

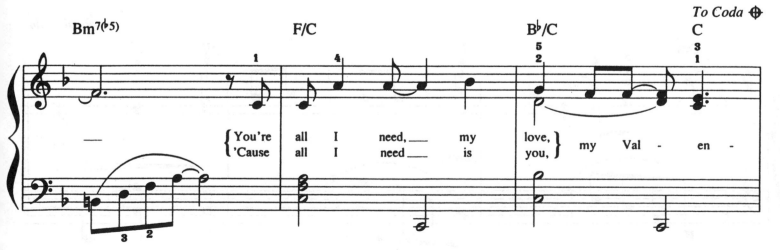

168

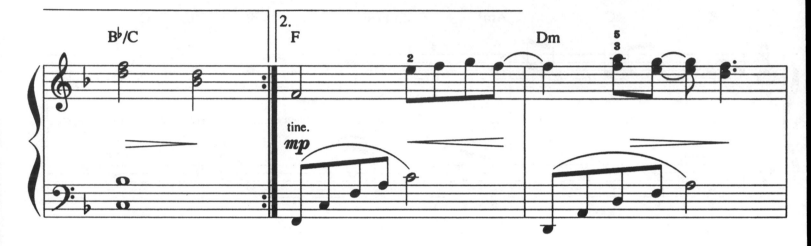

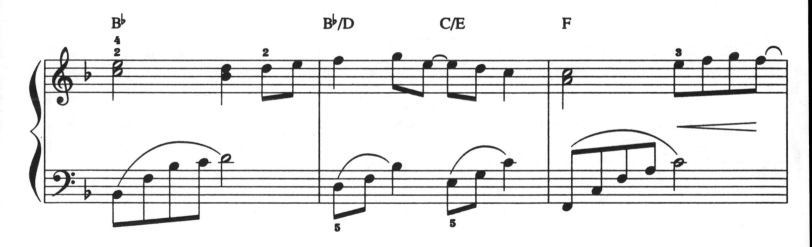

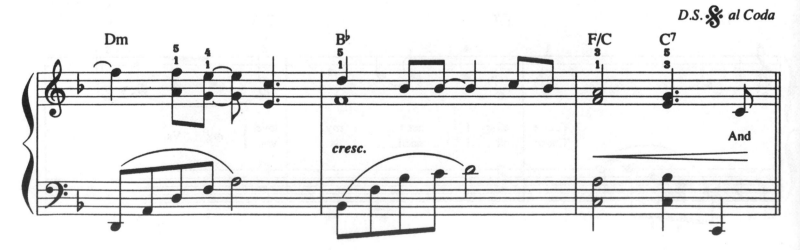

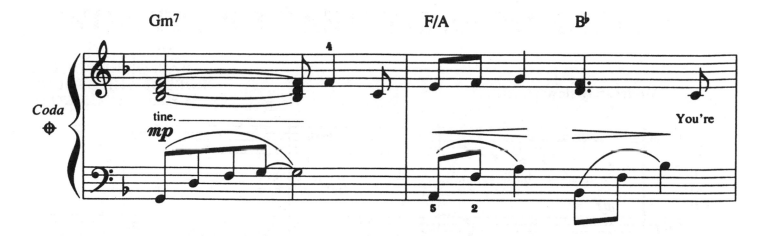

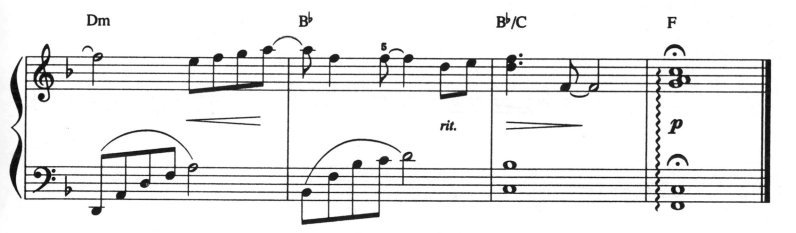

Verse 2:
All of my life,
I have been waiting for all you give to me.
You've opened my eyes
And shown me how to love unselfishly.
I've dreamed of this a thousand times before,
But in my dreams I couldn't love you more.
I will give you my heart until the end of time.
You're all I need, my love,
My Valentine.

WHERE DOES MY HEART BEAT NOW

Words and Music by
TAYLOR RHODES and
ROBERT WHITE JOHNSON
Arranged by DAN COATES

Moderately slow

1. So much to be-lieve in, _____ we were lost in _____ time. _____
2. Can-dle in the wa-ter _____ drift-ing help-less-ly, _____

mf

Ev-'ry-thing I need-ed _____ I felt in-to _____ your eyes. _____
hid-ing from the thun-der _____ come and res-cue me. _____

Al-ways thought of keep-in' _____ your heart next to _____ mine,
Driv-en by the hun-ger _____ of the end-less _____ dream,

but now _____ that seems so far a-way.
I'm search-ing for the hand that I can hold.

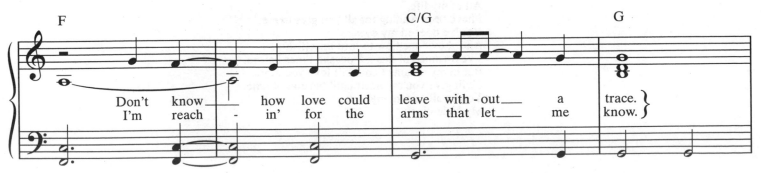

Don't know _____ how love could leave with-out _____ a trace. }
I'm reach-in' for the arms that let _____ me know.

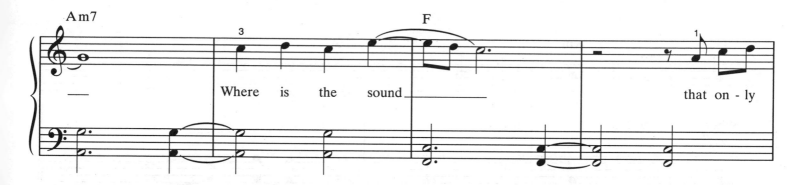

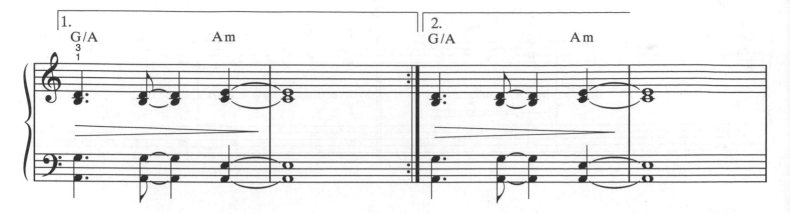

Where do the lone - ly hearts go?

Nah, nah, nah,— nah, nah. Nah, nah, nah,— nah,

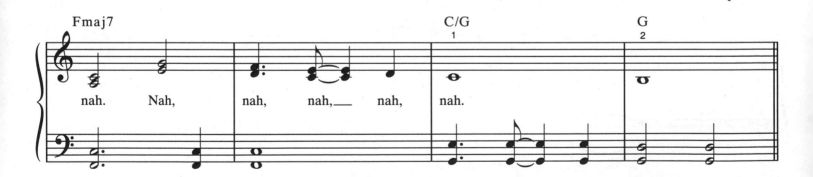

nah. Nah, nah, nah,— nah, nah.

Then one touch o - ver-comes the si - lence. Love still sur - vives._____

Two hearts a need - ing one an-oth-er give me wings to fly.

D.S. 𝄋 al Coda

cresc.

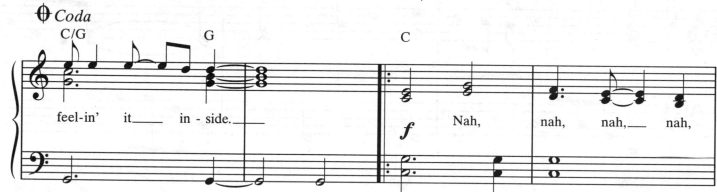

⊕ Coda

feel-in' it___ in - side.___ Nah, nah, nah,___ nah,

nah. Nah, nah, nah,___ nah, nah. Nah, nah, nah,___ nah,

nah.

1.   2.

sfz

WHEREVER YOU GO

Words and Music by
DURELL BOTTOMS, NICOLE RENEE
and MICHAEL McCRARY
Arranged by DAN COATES

ain't been the same.____ I'm use - less with - out ____ your love.____

I'm call - ing,__ cry - ing out your name.____ But when I

look a - round,_____ your love's no - where to ___ be found.

Please come back to me.____ You know__ you're my

175

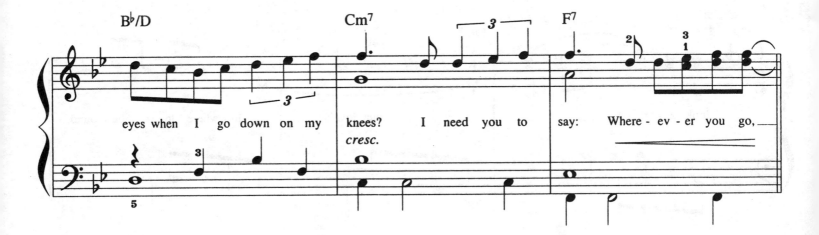

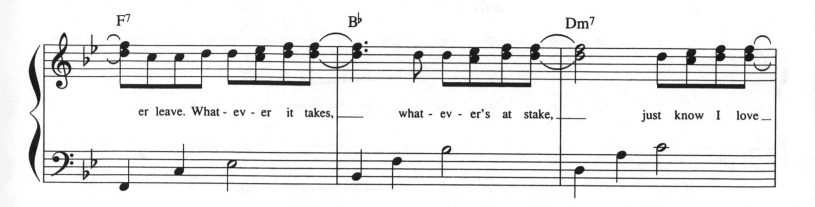

er leave. What - ev - er it takes, _____ what - ev - er's at stake, _____ just know I love

_____ you, and know I'll be _____ right here. And no mat - ter what _____ it

takes, I'll be wait - ing here _____ for you al -

ways. _____ right here.

178

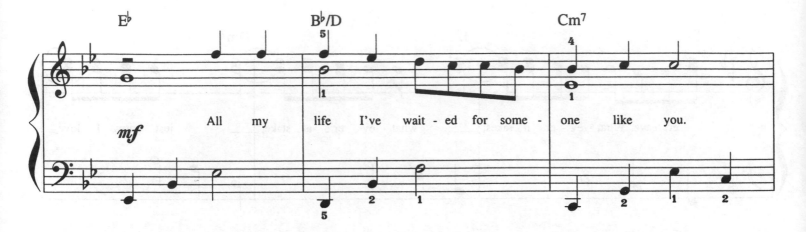

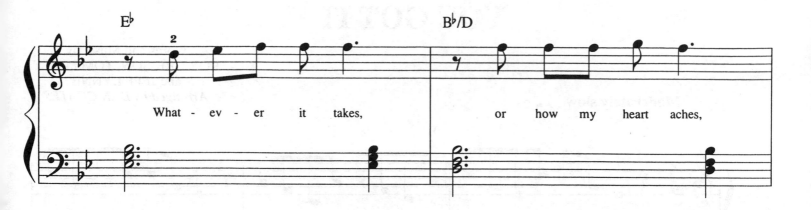

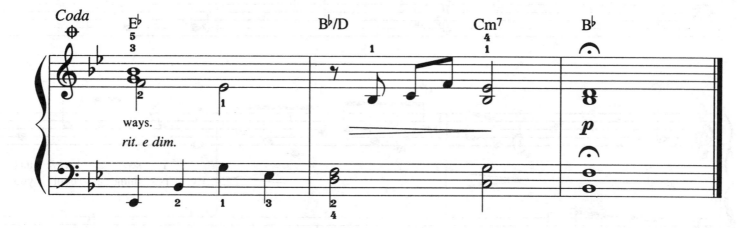

Verse 2:
Goodbye is such a hard thing to say
When you're all I know,
When you're my everything.
And who will stay and care for me?
When you're gone, I'll be all alone.
Who will come and comfort me
And fulfill my needs?
Who will love me?
Who will care?
Who will be there
When I need someone for me?
Who will be there to dry my eyes
When I go down on my knees?
I need you to say:
(To Chorus:)

YOU GOT IT

Words and Music by
ROY ORBISON, TOM PETTY
and JEFF LYNNE
Arranged by DAN COATES

Moderately slow ♩ = 88

Ev - 'ry time I look in - to your love - ly
Ev - 'ry time I hold you, I be - gin to un - der -

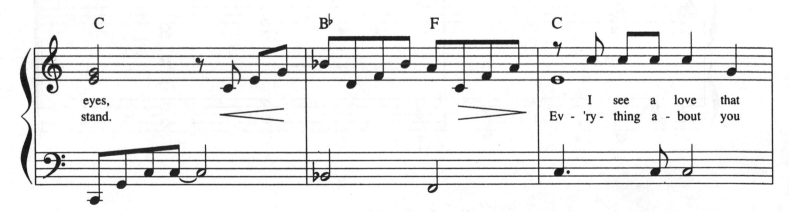

eyes,
stand.

I see a love that
Ev - 'ry - thing a - bout you

mon - ey just can't
tells me you're my

buy.
man.

One
I

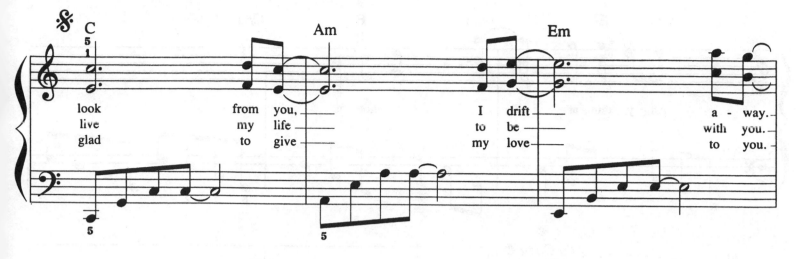

An - y - thing at all, _____ you got it, ba -

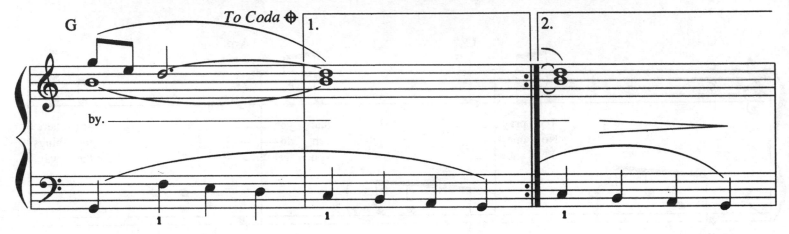

by. _____

An - y - thing you want, ___ an - y - thing you need,

___ an - y - thing at all. ___ I'm

YOU'LL SEE

Words and Music by
MADONNA CICCONE and
DAVID FOSTER
Arranged by DAN COATES

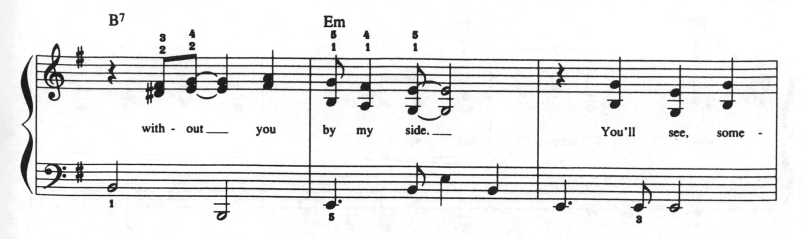

with - out ____ you by my side. ____ You'll see, some -

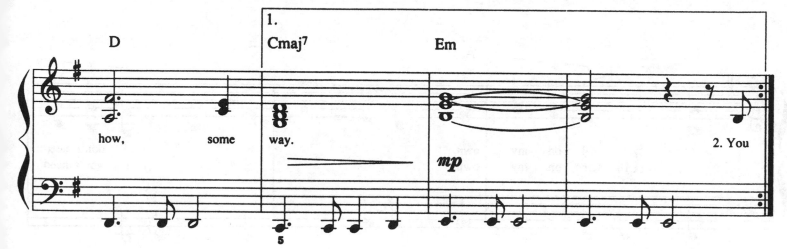

how, some way. 2. You

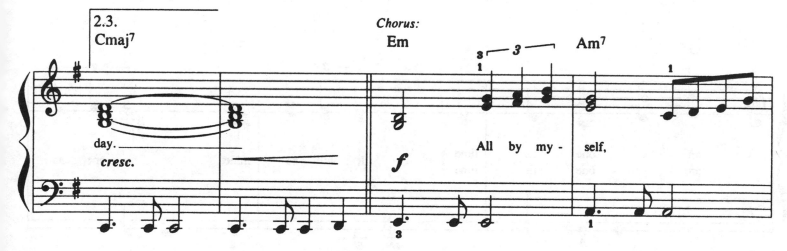

day. ____ All by my - self,

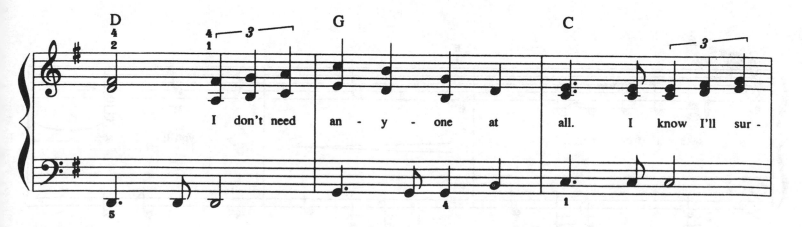

I don't need an - y - one at all. I know I'll sur -

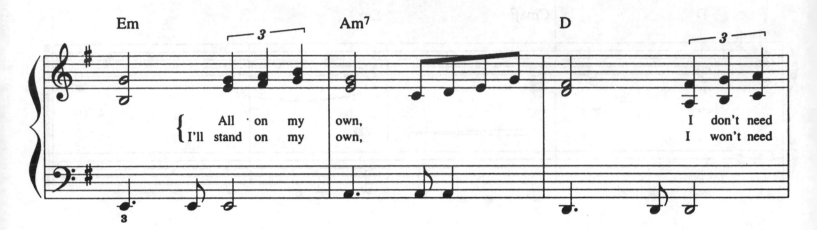

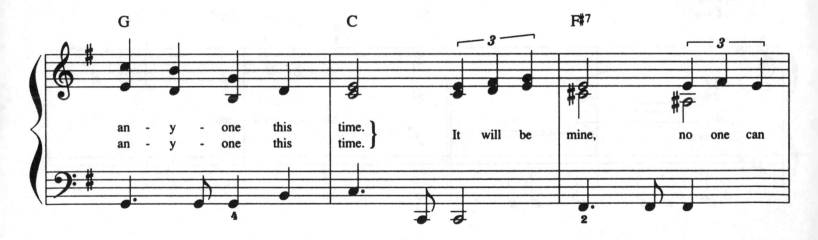

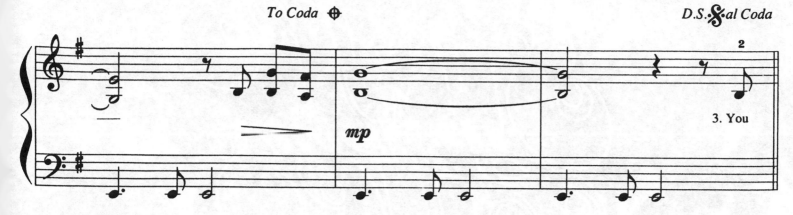

Verse 2:
You think that I can never laugh again,
You'll see.
You think that you've destroyed my faith in love.
You think after all you've done,
I'll never find my way back home.
You'll see, somehow, some day.   *(To Chorus:)*

Verse 3:
You think that you are strong, but you are weak,
You'll see.
It takes more strength to cry, admit defeat.
I have truth on my side,
You only have deceit.
You'll see, somehow, some day.   *(To Chorus:)*

7601A

7602A

7603A

8848A

8849A

8850A